Beloved on This Earth

Published by Brolga Publishing Pty Ltd
ABN 46 063 962 443
PO Box 12544
A'Beckett St
Melbourne, VIC, 8006
Australia

email: markzocchi@brolgapublishing.com.au

Copyright © 2014 Clive Broman
First Printing: 2013 Quickmatch Publishing
Cover Photo – Glasshouse Rocks Narooma (Clive Broman)
Back Cover – Photo by Ryan O'Toole

National Library of Australia
Cataloguing-in-Publication data

> *Beloved on this earth: Life, love, friendship and living with motor neurone disease/* Cheryl Fong; compiled by Clive Broman.
> 9781922175571 (paperback)
> Subjects: Fong, Cheryl.
>   Amyotrophic lateral
>   sclerosis--Patients--Australia--Biography.
>   Women--Australia--Biography.
> Dewey Number: 362.19683092

Printed in Australia
Cover design by Carl Broman (edited by Brolga Publishing)
Typesetting by Wanissa Somsuphangsri

BE PUBLISHED

Publish through a successful publisher. National distribution, Macmillan & International distribution to the United Kingdom, North America. Sales Representation to South East Asia
Email: markzocchi@brolgapublishing.com.au

Beloved on This Earth

Life, Love, Friendship and
Living with Motor Neurone Disease

❧

CHERYL FONG

FOREWORD BY DOMINIC ROWE

CONTRIBUTIONS BY CLIVE BROMAN

"And did you get what you wanted
from this life, even so?

I did

And what did you want?

To call myself beloved,
to feel myself beloved on the earth.

– Raymond Carter

DEDICATION

✥

I would like to thank all of the family and friends who have supported me over the last two and a half years since I was diagnosed with Motor Neurone Disease. In particular I thank my two boys Ashley and Paul who were the original motivation for this book and were happy for me to publish my story.

CONTENTS

CONTENTS

ACKNOWLEDGEMENTS

This book was never intended to be published and suffers from a lack of professional expertise. However, once it was decided to self-publish, a number of people offered to assist in bringing it up to scratch. Lydia Morton read the first draft and made many corrections. Mark and Joan Reiss, my California friends, spent time editing to improve the structure.

Carl Broman and Ryan O'Toole helped with the work needed for formatting and publishing. I did not have time to contact the many people mentioned in the book to inform them of their inclusion. I trust I have been honest and fair in what I have said about you. My husband Clive supported me through the process, encouraging me to include material about my life I had not considered. I am relying on him to do the final editing of this book. He also wrote a chapter to give his point of view.

When MND started to intrude on my ability to socialise the book became a great focus for me and gave me a sense of accomplishment.

I know I will probably never see the finished product but my boys have read the draft and it's a good feeling to know you have left something behind.

FOREWORD

It is a great honour to be asked to write the foreword for this book. This autobiography written by an extraordinary woman will touch every reader with its generosity, perception and kindness of spirit. I was fortunate to be the doctor, who along with Jenny Wray, was privileged to be involved in the management of Cheryl's care with Motor Neurone Disease, a disease that you would not wish on your worst enemy, let alone Cheryl.

I first met Cheryl and Clive in April 2011, referred by another neurologist to consider whether she had MND. It is one of the observations among neurologists that MND mostly happens to 'nice people' and so my heart started sinking as soon as we met, as a nicer person than Cheryl would be hard to find. Given her family history, we tried to track down the gene responsible for her MND after we confirmed the diagnosis. She faced each challenge of her MND with grace, good humour and tenacity. She and Clive focused on the challenge of living with MND, and squeezing the best out of every day, despite the accumulating problems.

I consider myself very fortunate to have been involved in Cheryl's care. It is even more humbling to read the telling of a remarkable life. I know that her story will touch every reader and, with that connection, Cheryl lives on in all of us who were fortunate enough to have her as a friend.

Dominic Rowe
Professor Dominic Rowe
AM BSc (Med), M.B.B.S. (Hons)
FRACP, PhD (UNSW)

INTRODUCTION

The first time I encountered someone with the slurred speech of Motor Neurone Disease (MND)[1] it was my father. We didn't have a clue what was wrong until he was diagnosed with MND and died within a year. It was thought, based on what he knew of his family's medical history, that he had sporadic MND, not familial or inherited. My brother and I went on with our lives, never thinking that MND would be an issue for either of us. In October 2010 I started slurring my words and for the next six months my husband Clive and I avoided facing up to the fact that I might have inherited MND. In March 2011 I was referred to a neurologist for tests. On April Fools Day 2011 a Canberra neurologist told us both that I most likely had familial MND and although it was really no surprise, it was devastating.

MND is a peculiar disease in that it doesn't follow a set pattern in any one case. It can start in your upper body ('PBP' or *Progressive Bulbar Palsy*) and take away your speech and your ability to swallow or it can commence with a gradual loss of function in a limb. No one can tell you how long you will live or even how the disease will progress. Some people die in a few months – Stephen Hawking, the British physicist, has been afflicted for 40 years. But on average you have two to three years.

---

1 MND is also referred to as Amyotrophic Lateral Sclerosis (ALS) in many parts of the world and as Lou Gehrig's disease in the USA.

There is no cure, virtually no treatment, except for a drug called Rilutek, which on average extends life by about three months, although it's hard to measure accurately the effect the drug has on any individual. Three months is not a long time, but you can do a lot in that time with the right mindset.

I have talked about MND in this book but it is a topic that others have written about with much greater expertise than me. My journey with it is very similar to that of others, not so much in physical symptoms, because they vary a lot, but certainly in my emotional response to loss of function.

I am aware that MND sufferers and newly diagnosed MND patients may have an interest in this story in the hope that there may be some information that will help on the journey. I certainly sought out and read a lot of material and some heart-rending personal stories from MND sufferers and I experienced a mix of emotions from that process. My message to those people, my MND brothers and sisters, is that each journey is different and you can take control early to make it a positive journey for you and those you leave behind. I hope what I have to say gives comfort and strength and maybe some practical tips about dealing with the relentless march of MND.

I can't pretend that it's not very confronting to know you are going to die. Most of us know that to be the case but we cope because there is the uncertainty of when and how it will happen. It is not on your mind on a daily basis. I realised very early that it was important to live with MND rather than battling against it. You use your energy to live the life you can rather than trying to maintain the life you had.

My neurologist Dominic Rowe told me early on that there are two things that get you in the end with MND: lack of adequate nutrition and respiration issues. I am fighting both at the moment. I know in my heart of hearts that unless I solve the feeding problem my time is limited. I have been busy putting my personal affairs in order including the final editing of this book.

Someone asked me recently if I am fearful of dying and, yes, I am but I hope that I will be brave enough to call an end when there is no quality of life left. I am getting close, as I am not too keen on socialising or leaving my home now. I am very tired after more than a year of communicating every feeling, need and conversation in writing. It is quite telling for me that I have almost (but not quite) given up caring about the maintenance of our home. I started writing this story as a long letter to my sons Paul and Ashley Fong. However, a number of people said I should write about myself and my experience with MND. So I used what I had written for them as the basis for this story, adding and deleting as appropriate.

I had a life, before my MND became active, that was much more interesting. While I haven't written about every aspect of my life, (some things remain too personal for general consumption) I think I have written enough to mark that I was here. If, dear reader, you found it interesting to read about my ordinary life, I thankyou.

CHAPTER 1

A Brief History of My Early Years

I was born in Fairfield, Melbournes on 18 June 1946 and named Cheryl Moon. It was not that long after WWII had ended and that put me in the first of the baby boomers cohort. When I was eighteen months old, Mum and Dad moved from Northcote, Melbourne, back to Wonthaggi in south west Gippsland, Victoria. I am not sure what prompted this but it may have been that Dad had been released from service in the Royal Australian Air Force (RAAF). During the war he was based at Laverton and worked on repairing aircraft so did not see active service. Both of my parents grew up in Wonthaggi and their fathers were coal miners.

I started out as an only child until I was eight. That's when my brother Brian was born. But before me my parents had a boy (Alan) who died shortly after birth, then me and after me another boy (Reginald) who also died shortly after birth. My mother had at least one miscarriage, maybe more, so a lot of heartbreak for them.

When my mother was pregnant with Brian the doctor put her into hospital at three months so she could have complete bed rest. The only problem was that they put her into the maternity ward and in those days children were not allowed to visit. Dad was working as a barman at the

Workmen's Club so did not work regular hours. I stayed with family friends while he was working and only went home when he had days off. Mum and I used to write letters to each other and once a month they let me in to see her. There was a German woman who was the head nurse and she would hold my hand from the entrance to where Mum was and I always remembered that she had very cold hands.

Came the day that Brian was born, or rather early morning, and the doctor knocked on our door to tell Dad that he had a son. So off he went to the hospital telling me he would be straight back, so I sat on the front verandah in my nightdress waiting for him and what does he do, but drive straight past our house. He went to tell the friends who had minded me that they had a boy. It is funny the things that stay in your mind.

It isn't only the Chinese who place emphasis on having a son. Australian men weren't much different back then. Mum was weak and needed help when she came home so I became the helper. Dad was never much good at that which I think Mum resented all of her life. Later in my early teens Grandma Moon came to live with us. Brian and I really loved her but apparently she had not been so liked by all of her daughters-in-law. She had been a widow since I was two years old and lived alone, but of course the time came when she couldn't manage anymore and none of the others would take her so she came to us, that is, Mum and me.

Mum really resented it as she was also working as a sales assistant at Coles where she later became the head of all the sales assistants. Mum had a really strong work ethic, which had been instilled in her as one of twelve kids, eight girls and four boys. Her mother, who we called "Margie"(a name given to her by one of my older cousins as a child), mainly looked after babies and cooked while the girls did the housework. Their father was a very stern man of Germanic background who worked as a coal miner. When there were accidents or strikes the pay was short and Mum always talked of eating bread and dripping (that was lard which had had meat roasted in it where the drippings enhanced the flavor of the lard). So she knew tough times and hunger. They slept three to a double bed. If they misbehaved during the day, father hauled the guilty one out of bed when he came home from his shift and she would get a beating with a strap.

Mum's early experience influenced her to always buy butter, never margarine, good quality canned goods, and meat. When we misbehaved Brian and I were never punished by being sent to bed without our dinner. The other thing about Mum was that she was scrupulously clean. In those days you scrubbed floors and then polished them on your hands and knees. So that's what I had to do as a teenager since Mum was working. Even when society had moved on to mopping floors, our floors were still done on hands and knees, mainly mine. I also cooked the dinner at night after school, chopped wood and coal to light the fire and the hot water boiler, fed the chooks and looked after Brian. Dad by this time had his own plumbing business and after work there was always a stopover at the pub.

I still remember the odd occasions when for some reason Mum was home during the week or Dad had decided to give the pub a miss, coming home to the smell of food being cooked. Just another funny memory!

My upbringing wasn't all tough. When I was young, we used to go camping after Christmas in huts at Flat Rocks beach on the coastal road between Cape Paterson and Inverloch. We would eat freshly caught crayfish and whoppers since there were no restrictions on size or bag limits. I remember finding a dead fairy penguin on the beach and being very upset when Dad buried it in the hole he had dug to bury the contents of our toilet drum. We didn't own a hut but had the use of one owned by friends. The huts were nestled amongst trees just over the dunes and before the road. I just loved it and always wanted to eventually have a house on that road. The huts are long gone and the area between Inverloch and Flat Rocks is just about full of houses. That type of camping, is in the past. I am so lucky since for the last eleven years, I have lived in the gorgeous coastal town of Narooma, my dream place now.

I was brought up to be well-mannered, even having to call adult family friends Aunty and Uncle. I was fairly shy but did well at school. For some reason Mum sent me to elocution lessons when I was about five. I don't remember how long I did it for, but the result was that I had very clear diction. What I do recall was, walking to my teacher's house, and often passing Italian men carrying sugar bags — probably containing rabbits or birds. Many Italian men who migrated to Australia after WWII, worked in the coal mines. My problem was that being so young I was frightened of them and worried that one day I might get put in a bag!

Wonthaggi was a unique small town with a population of about 6,000 when I was growing up. It was established in 1910 as a coal mining town and had strong union membership. The coal seams were only about eighteen inches thick so the miners could not use machinery. They mined the coal with pick and shovel. There were often cave-ins causing serious injury and sometimes death. The town had a substantial hospital so that miners who were injured could receive immediate treatment.

There were often strikes by the early miners, like my grandfathers, for better working conditions. The miner's union established a co-operative grocery store and a picture theatre called the Union Theatre.

Town life moved according to the mine whistle which blew for the change of each shift. In the summer the miner's union would put on a picnic day at Inverloch with free buses to get families there since few people had their own car. There would be races, a lunch for every kid that was presented in a brown paper bag, lollies, ice creams, and not very politically correct bathing beauty competitions. I won one once, great claim to fame! It's amazing as a kid what you take as normal, like the mine whistle, and you don't realise that not every small town has one. I got an early introduction into both unionism and scab labour. I was always a union member my entire working life.

I loved to read. Books were my friends and took me to other worlds outside of little old Wonthaggi. I also loved movies for the same reasons. Most of them were from Hollywood and everything about American life seemed so exciting. They were always so clean and well dressed. It was not long after the war, and there were lots of war movies. I was very impressionable in my early teens and took all of the atrocities to heart, especially what had happened to the Jews. A lot of the books I read at that time were stories about the war, both in Europe and the Pacific. I had a very romantic notion of Israel for years and which lasted even after I visited there but nowadays I can't support what they do.

My teenage years were pretty turbulent emotionally. It was a combination of burgeoning hormones, Hollywood movies, Mum and Dad very unhappy and fighting a lot, and me being required to run the house and mind Brian and Grandma.

I had more responsibility than Eileen who came from a family of twelve and was my closest friend since we met around age three. Even though she went to the Catholic school and I went to the state school, we formed a friendship that has lasted all of our lives. We spent many hours just doing mundane things together, like minding her mother's cows or the younger kids. We roamed the paddocks and the nearby pine forest and made cubby houses and just generally hung out together. She has loved me unconditionally all of my life and for that I am truly thankful.

Mum had to work at a young age, so she didn't see why it should be any different for me. She wasn't good at school so she left at fourteen and went to work. I enjoyed school and learning. In my six years at high school I was a Form Captain, House Captain (that was for sport) a Prefect and finally the Head Girl Prefect. My aunty, Alma Moon, was a teacher at the school. She taught commercial subjects so never taught me but she was House Mistress while I was Captain of Paterson House.

I did OK up to Fourth Form but then made the mistake of doing physics, chemistry and Math 1 and 2, which I just wasn't cut out for. I failed my Leaving Certificate that year. I went back the next year and did humanities and passed. I can't remember if it was that year or the first year of my Leaving Certificate that Mum left home and went to Melbourne just around study and exam time. So my first priority was to run the home. Dad eventually found her and she came home but they didn't ever make peace. There was always an undercurrent in our house just waiting for hostilities to break out.

Sadly, they fought a lot and usually at the dinner table. A couple of times I remember vividly. Once when Dad was so enraged about having sausages for dinner that he hit his plate with such force his whole meal bounced over the table. I also remember Mum throwing the butter and jam from the table and hitting the wall. She probably wasn't game to actually hit Dad with it. I used to try and leave the table but Dad would always make me sit down. Then he would go off to bed and leave us shattered, or at least I was. I began to think it was my fault as they say kids often do. When I finally left home at the end of school I thought it would be better but of course it was not.

I was at the age of wanting to go to the local dance or the movies on Saturday night with Eileen but it depended on whether Mum and Dad were home. They often went to the pub and would phone me to say they were staying on, so that was the end of any plans I might have had. I had to feed Grandma and Brian, also get him bathed and into bed. He used to play up on me and I had to chase him around to get his clothes off. It's no wonder with eight years difference in age and having to mind him all the time that I built up some resentment towards him. We were never close in later years. He came to live with David (my first husband) and I after cyclone Tracy, he used to spoil my two boys. He was a great uncle, and he was always playing epic games of backyard cricket with them.

I was a Life Saver in the Cape Paterson juniors and got all of my certificates including my Bronze Medallion and Bronze Cross. Once you had a Bronze Cross you did it again and got a bar put on it. I loved it but when it came time for me to join the seniors Mum wouldn't let me because she thought I would get into "trouble", little did she know it would happen anyway. It would have been better to let me join and experience life in familiar surroundings. I was still able to play hockey in the winter and Mum was the coach of the Wonthaggi High Old Girls team. It was the only sport other than swimming that I was any good at.

I only learned to swim in Grade Six, as I was terrified of the water, having nearly drowned in the surf at Flat Rocks when I was small. I was also terrified when we had swimming lessons at school. I eventually taught myself in about a foot of water. I suddenly got off the bottom and was on my way with dog- paddle. I always loved the sea and in the summer holidays I got to hitchhike with Eileen out to Cape Paterson. Hitchhiking was quite safe, as we knew all the people driving by. We would spend the whole day either at the bay or the surf beach, where the boys were. Later in high school I had a crush on a guy who didn't reciprocate so I went around with a broken heart for a couple of years.

I went to both primary and secondary school with a boy called Jethro (Jeff) Wittig. In high school he used to walk home with his girlfriend who was my neighbour and often I was with them. He tracked me down after cyclone Tracy and we renewed our friendship. By then we were both married with children. We eventually lost touch until in 1993 they had a "Back to Wonthaggi Primary School" planned and we met up again through that. We have managed not to lose touch again and Jeff and his partner Deanna have become dear and devoted friends.

CHAPTER 2

Moving to Darwin

When leaving school I didn't know what to do next. Around that time Dad had decided he wanted to move and decided on Darwin. I was thinking about nursing when there was an advert in the Darwin paper for student nurses, so I applied and got in. I had hardly ever been away from home before, just a couple of visits alone to my uncle and aunty in Box Hill and even then I got homesick. I was definitely not very experienced in the world and then I was off to Darwin in my first plane ride. Eileen came with Mum and Dad to see me off and she cried buckets.

The trip took about twelve hours then as they stopped in Alice Springs, Tennant Creek and Katherine. When we arrived the terminal was really just a tin shed and the runway was actually the RAAF runway and used by civilian aircraft as well. It was later expanded to be a more substantial terminal and in the late 1980s was demolished and a new one built on a different site but still on the RAAF runway. There was a Chinese guy there to meet us, as unbeknownst to me, there were other student nurses on the flight. He had a list and I was called out as Nurse Moon. I also remember the smell of frangipani and gardenias in the air and, as it was April, it was very humid. It was like being in another country.

We were taken to the sisters' quarters at Larrakeyah where there was a room with about eight hospital beds with mosquito nets around them. That was where I first met my friend Pinky. Her name was June but she looked like an American actress who played a character called Pinky so that's who she became. Her father was a station manager in the Kimberlys around Derby and she had been sent to boarding school in Perth so she tried to help me with my desperate homesickness. I even called Mum and said I wanted to come home. She said Dad would be angry and what about all of the presents I had been given. I said "I'll give them back" but it was never going to happen. Just as well really as I did get over it and went on to become a good nurse.

I did think people were friendly in Darwin as we got invitations to the various hostels and messes around town, the army, police, bank officers, etc. but I came to understand that this was about a new supply of women arriving in Darwin. Women were in short supply in this frontier town.

The old Darwin hospital had segregated wards that fanned out from a grassy quadrangle with covered verandahs leading to them. On Friday nights they would show a movie in the quadrangle and we would get as many of the patients as we could there; we even wheeled their beds out. There were only four places in the hospital that had air-conditioning; the operating theatre, the maternity delivery room, the Central Sterilizing Department (CSD) and the morgue. You would go to work with your starched uniform and cap on and by the end of your shift they would be limp with sweat. Of course it was not so bad in the dry season.

There were a lot of characters at the hospital, both patients and staff. My first morning on the wards was in the men's medical ward. There was an old man who had been in hospital since 1945, the year before I was born. He used to put poo in the drawer of his bedside table. That morning I had to give him a bath with the assistance of an orderly called Morrie. Morrie was running the bath as I wheeled Darkie in to the bathroom. The tap was running and Morrie was pouring a huge amount of Dettol into the water saying, "Darkie has a bath that is 99% Dettol". I was horrified. But worse, Morrie got a call to take the ambulance out and I was left with Darkie who I had to undress, the first time I saw an adult naked male. All the while he kept saying, "You won't send me home, will you, girlie".

Some of the sisters-in-charge were legends in their own time. All had idiosyncrasies that we used to mock for amusement. I even nursed, our friend Tom Calma's grandfather, Edwin Verburg. The bridge over the Adelaide River is named for him. He stays in my memory because one day while assisting to lift him up I knocked his sputum mug over and it went all down the back of my legs. That topped Darkie's bath for horrific events. Darwin really was the last frontier back then.

One thing that does stay in my memory was the racial segregation in the hospital. There was a senior sister from South Africa who used to refer to the Aboriginal patients as "damn kaffirs". I must say I found the Aboriginal people much easier to nurse than the more demanding "whites". Traditional Aboriginal people I have always found to be decent, easy-going and non-judgmental. It was a pleasure to nurse them.

Mum, Dad and Brian had arrived in Darwin in November 1964. They had driven and Mum was ill on the way with what turned out to be pneumonia so she wasn't in great shape. They house sat for a while as people would go on long leave and needed their houses to be maintained. Eventually they got a two-bedroom unit in a new Housing Commission development in Mitchell Street within walking distance of the town centre.

I was still living in at the hospital but I could always get a pass to stay overnight to visit them. In those days they used to do a bed check to make sure you were in bed. We used to put pillows in Pinky's bed for the bed check. We had a way of removing louvres from the uniform room window so we could squeeze in and haul ourselves to the floor by hanging on to the big wooden dirty uniform bin. I did go home sometimes, but not nearly as often as I had passes.

Mum had started drinking in Wonthaggi, but just socially. Her drinking moved to a new level in Darwin. After a fight Dad would go to bed and Mum had a female friend who lived alone downstairs and she would go there and drink with her. Eventually Mum became a functioning alcoholic and it was sad to see her being sneaky about her drinking. She left Dad a couple of times in Darwin but because she remained in Darwin he always found her and she went back. I believe that there was physical violence on a few occasions but thankfully I never saw it although Brian probably did.

Dad was an intelligent man but he had never had the

opportunity to do anything with his smarts. He did not want to go down the mine to work so he apprenticed as a plumber. I think he was always deeply frustrated and bitter about his life and he took it out on his family. Once when Mum left him she came to me and my future husband David Fong. I could not turn her away but Dad accused me of wanting her there to do my housework. When I told him that I was engaged to be married his only comment was that there were enough half-caste children in the world (David was ethnic Chinese). I was not pregnant but Dad knew how to push people's buttons to hurt.

CHAPTER 3

Getting Pregnant and the Decision to Keep My Baby

There were thirteen of us in my training school and gradually each one left due to pregnancy. I was the last woman standing but at Pinky's wedding I met Paul's father. We were an item for quite a while but he was a keen sailor and went away to an interstate sailing competition and when he came back he broke it off. It turned out to be too late for me as I was already pregnant with Paul. I had done all of my training but had one exam and then finals to do but they wouldn't let me stay on to qualify.

Mum's mother was dying of cancer in Wonthaggi so Mum and Dad decided to drive down, taking Brian and me. I had my twenty-first birthday on the road somewhere between Katherine and Tennant Creek. It was a hoot!!! While in Melbourne, Dad had me phoning abortion places but fortunately none of them would take me. He was concerned that I would ruin our good name. I kept thinking 'What good name?' hardly anybody knows us in Darwin! We stayed at my uncle's place in Box Hill for a while and then we went to Wonthaggi. While there we heard that my cousin Heather had had German measles. I was rushed off to a doctor to get a shot of gamma globulin, which I still remember hurt like hell, to prevent me from getting them as they could cause harm to a baby in the first three months of gestation. It turned out to be useless as on the way back to Darwin I woke up with spots on my face and I was still under the three months stage. That was most likely the cause of Paul's dyslexia.

I remained in Darwin living with Mum and Dad and Brian in their two-bedroom flat in Mitchell Street until October 1967 when I was sent off to Melbourne, this time to a home for unmarried mothers. It was in Station Street, Fairfield, and apparently I was born in a small hospital in that street. Only my uncle and aunty and Eileen knew that I was there. What a place. The Matron gave me a religious lecture on arrival and I told her that I was not religious and couldn't care less if the lord loved me. She also said that as there was already a Cheryl in the place I would have to go by another name and I refused, so I think they changed the name of the other girl. We all had to provide a set of clothes for our babies and I chose carefully so that whoever got my baby would somehow know that I cared. Most of the girls there were very young, still teenagers, and some used to sneak out at night, climb the fence and meet their boyfriends. Because I was older and not from Melbourne I could occasionally go and spend the day with my aunty in Box Hill. My uncle used to come and take me out on weekends and buy me gelati.

I gave birth to my baby boy in the Royal Women's Hospital and I was supposed to give him up for adoption. In that case, I was never to see him again but one of the nurses brought him to me and I got to cuddle him on a couple of occasions. I went home from hospital to my uncle's place and other family members were told I had come over from Adelaide to visit. Another uncle was visiting for the day from Wonthaggi and there was a game of cricket played with my younger cousins in the park and of course I was expected to play too. I had to run and chase the ball after having had stitches from the birth but of course none of them knew about my baby.

Before returning to Darwin, I went to a Methodist babies home and gave my written consent to adoption. There was a thirty-day cooling-off period in which you could revoke your consent. I went back to Darwin feeling so miserable. Some friends offered to foster Paul, so that I could eventually have him. This enabled me to finally stand up to Dad and I revoked my consent. Mum went down to Melbourne as her mother had died and she picked Paul up from the babies home and took him back to her brother's place. They were the aunt and uncle who had been so supportive, during my stay in the unmarried mother's home.

Paul had not put on much weight so they fed him up and Mum brought him home to Darwin. I had found a job in a shop and started working five weeks after the birth. Luckily, I got the woman in the flat next door to have Paul during the day as Mum was working at the hospital. Paul, Brian and I shared a room until I moved out into a caravan behind a house a little further away. It was on the block next door to what was then the Koala Motel. I also found an older lady to look after Paul and she dearly loved him.

CHAPTER 4

Life as a Single Working Mum

I eventually got a temporary government job through my friend Marie who worked in the Commonwealth Employment Service (CES). We weren't friends then, but a few years later she and I worked together and that was when we became friends. She was divorced and her kids used to go to their father on Christmas Day so she always spent it with David and me after I was married.

In the early days we lived in the caravan and I would drop Paul off to the babysitter in the pusher and then go back and get my motor scooter. I had a 50cc Yamaha, which I bought when I was nursing and had moved out of the nursing home into a flat in Fannie Bay with another nurse. Eventually, I had to move Paul into family day care in Parap so that is when I got a car. I would drive to Parap and drop Paul off and then drive back into town to work. The lady running the day care had been my tutor as a student nurse so she had a nursing background.

I had only driven Dad's automatic Holden and even though I got my licence for a manual car I wasn't much good at driving one. Also in those days baby car seats were really just canvas on a frame that a child could sit in with absolutely no protection. So the first time I drove it with Paul in the car seat, I drove straight into the tree in front of the caravan. We weren't hurt but the front of the car was a bit bent.

My first clerical job was in the Department of the Northern Territory, Public Utilities Section. It was where people signed up for electricity, water and sewage. We had guys who would go out to read the meters then we would arrange the billing through the Finance Section. This was where my future husband, brother-in-law and sister-in-law worked and that is how I got to know them. The work environment was very relaxed in those days so you always had time for a chat. We even had tea ladies who used to bring a trolley around at morning and afternoon teatime. All public servants worked from 8 am till 4.21 pm with an hour for lunch. They used to rule a line in red in the "sign in" book at two minutes past eight.

One time I got to work and realized that I had left Paul's bottles at home so I went cap in hand and asked if I could make the round trip home and get the bottles to the babysitter. While everything was quite regulated, people were kind and found ways around procedures where necessary. I became permanent and got a promotion from Base Grade Clerk to Clerk Class 2/3 at the Department of Health, in the Recruitment Section. Ironically, I was involved in recruiting student nurses, trained nurses, doctors, and other allied health professionals. At that time there was little private practice in the health area in Darwin. Health was located in Mitchell Street in an old house on the Esplanade for the senior staff and in tin huts left over from the war for the rest of the staff. They had fans but no air-conditioning so the after-lunch period was awful as you spent most of your time trying not to fall asleep. I eventually got a promotion back to the Department of

NT in the Recruitment Section. The office was located in the Civic Centre in Harry Chan Avenue and, blissfully, it had air-conditioning.

By this time I had been going out with David Fong since late 1969. I don't really know why he was interested in me as I was nearly four years older than him and had a child. David's oldest sister Joan was very worried about it. While I was still nursing she came back from working overseas and was in charge of the Aboriginal children's ward. So I had worked with her and also with another future sister-in-law Eli who had trained in Adelaide and married there but returned to Darwin through her husband's employment.

Paul and I moved out of the van, once I got a government job, into a new flat in Smith Street, quite close to the Uniting Church. From there we moved into a house in Manton Street, right in the heart of China Town. Brian Chin, who was a good mate of David's, was dating the girl who lived next door to me. Her mother ran a Chinese restaurant out at Winnellie and her grandmother also lived with them. She was a bent little woman who had obviously lived most of her life in China because she spoke only Cantonese. She went out and played Mah Jong for hours. I never knew her name, we just referred to her as Grandma.

Grandma used to climb over the fence to get the ashes from our burning-off to put on her garden. The fence was only a metre high and made of pig wire and she was too old to be doing that, so if I saw her I would tell her to stay there and get the ashes for her. She also used to come over and knock on the floor with a broom from under the house to get my attention. One day she gave me a bag of sugar and another time some of those rice things wrapped in banana leaves. I used to bring her up the stairs and she would have a small glass of green ginger wine.

We did quite a lot of camping and fishing trips at that time. David and his brother Tom used to go crabbing and each would get a sugar bag full since no bag limits existed then. While we lived there, a cyclone took off part of our roof - that was the wet season before Cyclone Tracy. Paul started school at the historic Darwin Primary School and I remember helping to make sartees for the school stall at the Darwin Show with people like Joe Sarab and some of the Chin family.

It was a lovely surprise to run into Joe Sarab and Norm Chin at the Chung Wah Society Museum on my last trip to Darwin. They are both in their seventies now and look as fit as ever and we had quite a talk about the old days. We were showing our friends Lydia and Doug the "Sweet and Sour" exhibition on the life of Chinese in the Northern Territory. The Fong family features prominently in the exhibition; there are photos of their life as market gardeners near Pine Creek. There are photos of Mr and Mrs Fong working with their five girls harvesting cabbages and other vegetables. There is also a display of the old farming implements that they used.

CHAPTER 5

Joining the Fong Family

David and I married in June 1972. We had a civil ceremony at the Registry Office in Harry Chan Avenue. That was pretty significant because Harry Chan was the first Chinese person to be elected mayor of a town in Australia. He was also the Leader of the Legislative Assembly, and Mrs Fong's brother. I knew of him, but we never met as he had died before I met David.

We celebrated with a family dinner at the Fannie Bay Hotel. Afterwards we went to a ball at the outdoor entertaining area at the Civic Centre, which allowed us to celebrate with friends. In those days, each government department held a ball in the dry season and they were pretty grand affairs for which the girls needed a new dress and guys were required to wear long pants and a dress shirt and tie which was called Darwin Rig. The ticket price included a meal and drinks. The meals were all pretty lavish – prawns and Chinese food and all you could drink. There weren't any drunk driving laws then either. Once they were introduced, most of the balls ended.

During this period David adopted Paul. We were interviewed at home by a social worker and she clearly thought David was too immature to be a father. Since we were married it all went through and Paul officially became a Fong too.

Our life was fairly simple in those days, (lots of fishing and camping trips). There were visits to my parents and to the Fongs where we often used to have meals. Granny (Mrs Fong) always had something from the garden to give us, (vegetables, pawpaws and mangoes). There were two cinemas in Darwin at the time. One was called the Star Theatre, located in Smith Street. When I arrived in Darwin in 1964, white people sat upstairs and full-blood Aboriginals and coloured people (which were the terms used back then for mixed race people) sat downstairs. There was also a cinema at Parap, which had corrugated iron walls and kids would run by with a stick and make a hell of a racket. It was customary then to play the National Anthem before the film was run and when you stood up the canvas seats used to flap back and make a terrible noise. Later there was the drive-in theatre at Nightcliff, which was very popular in the dry season.

In July 1974 we moved to a new government house in Nakara. We wanted to buy a house and the government was not selling the old houses in town like ours in Manton Street. When they built the houses in the northern suburbs, they completely cleared the blocks so you had just bare dirt. To plant a lawn you had to get in loads of soil and go to friends' established houses to get lawn runners to plant. It was a hand-and-knees job planting them. Nakara was such a new suburb that the primary school wasn't opened yet so Paul went to Tiwi Primary. School was a nightmare for him, as he had so much trouble learning and none of the teachers seemed to have a clue, and neither did I unfortunately.

CHAPTER 6

Cyclone Tracy

Christmas Eve 1974 was on a weekday, so David and I were at work in town. There was rain and it was windy and there was talk around town that there was a cyclone in the Arafura Sea and that it was likely to hit Darwin. Most of us were pretty complacent about it as there had been cyclones before with lots of trees blown over and roof damage. Everybody went about business as usual ,that is, they had their work Christmas parties in the afternoon. I remember bumping into my brother Brian at lunchtime, in Smith Street Woolies. We talked about the rumours going around town that this cyclone was a big one and that it was going to hit Darwin.

David and I went home at the usual time. I cleaned the house and cooked rice as I always did on Christmas Eve. Our standard Christmas fare was lots of prawns, a ham, fried rice and salad. We had an artificial tree all decorated and Paul was hoping for a bike from Santa. He liked to leave a drink and a sandwich for Santa as long as it wasn't left in his room. I had told him that Santa gets so much Christmas cake that he would welcome a sandwich from somebody. I usually ate it as my dinner as I was so busy preparing for the next day.

It was raining and the wind was intense but we didn't get too worried until they said on the radio to tape up the windows and to fill the bath with water, presumably so we would have drinking water. But the tape wouldn't stick to the louvres and the water was pouring in so I kept trying to mop it up and throw it down the bath. We eventually rang the emergency number, triple O, and they said, to go to the nearest school. We grabbed Paul out of bed in his pajamas. David was dressed in pajama pants and I had on a nylon nightdress. We didn't get dressed, just put raincoats on.

Earlier in the day, we had called in on Granny and Grandpa Fong and for some reason had borrowed their orange Toyota. I guess David and Tom were going to use it to go fishing over the holidays. We had a blue Holden sedan (I can't remember the model) but when we went under the house and started it up we noticed that the Toyota had slipped in the mud and was blocking the driveway. So we got out and got the keys to the Toyota and got in that. However in our panic, we didn't see that we had left the lights on and the windscreen wipers going in the Holden.

Nakara Primary School was new and hadn't opened yet, so we headed for the Casuarina police station and parked out the front. By this time there was debris flying around and the wind was very strong. David grabbed Paul and took him inside while I was hanging on to the door handle waiting for him to come back for me but then I realised he wasn't coming so I let go, fully expecting to be blown away, but I made it to the door OK. Cyclone Tracy had wind speeds recorded at over 250 kph. When we arrived it was only the police and their families there, but by morning the station was full.

The police obviously had some idea of the extent of the damage and, as most of us were in pajamas, they said go over to Casuarina Shopping Square and get some clothes. I got a simple cotton dress and I remember looking at the price tag, then realised there was no way to pay for it so what did it matter. It is hard to remember everything from that time but we must have been able to get back to the house, and saw that it was gone. We had half a floor and a bath but no walls and our possessions were blown away or under the debris. Things that were under the Christmas tree fell out in one place so we found Paul's bike.

I remember David asking me if I had seen which way his aluminium dinghy had gone, as it had been stored under the house. For about two years after the cyclone, every time he saw an aluminium dinghy on top of a four-wheel drive, he maintained it was his! That used to drive me mad.

We then went in search of our families. There was a narrow path that had been cleared with bulldozers down Trower Road by mid- morning, so we were able to drive to Fannie Bay where we found that all of the Fong's were safe. We then went to look for my parents and Brian at the Darwin High School where Dad was the caretaker. All we found at the house was destruction but no bodies and we eventually found them at the school. They had taken shelter in the Home Economics flat of the Darwin High School, so they were OK.

We went back to Granny's where they had an old wood stove going and Granny was making winter melon soup and rice. Their old house had weathered the storm fine compared to all of the new houses out in the northern suburbs, like Nakara and Tiwi, many of them blown apart by flying debris. The houses were on piers so the wind just got under them and blew them away.

When we went back to try and sort through the rubble, we met our friends Julie and Doug Kinter. They had sheltered under the house across the road from our house and, because the car was lit up, they shouted out to us all night. That explained why the battery was flat in the car. I remember David telling me to pick up the downed power lines on our land so he could drive the Toyota in and I said " what if they are alive", but of course they weren't as all of the town's power had been knocked out. I also remember that we didn't have any water with us so we drank warm Coke after first washing the dirt from the can.

There was a funny story about the car under the house. Weeks later when David went out to the house site he found parts of the car missing, like the tyres and the doors. When he drove back to the Fong's house in Bayview Street, Fannie Bay, he happened to look down the driveway of the house across the road and saw the parts of our car. It was a bit of poetic justice for the thieves. David knew the family, and also that they had a penchant for theft.

The authorities were worried about disease breaking out so they called for all women and children to leave. We couldn't all stay at Fannie Bay, so Paul and I left on 30 of December on a Hercules transport to Adelaide. Some people went out on commercial planes but we drew the short straw and were packed in like sardines. Mind you, I do believe a 747 left Darwin with over 700 people on board so I would not have liked to have been on that flight.

When we got to Adelaide they had heaps of clothes that you could go through to get something warm to wear. They hadn't been sorted out so you just had to grab something and hope it would fit. The trousers I got for Paul were too big around the waist so I tied them up with a piece of rope. I had a pair of red-and-white checked slacks and an orange shirt. We really looked stylish! I had also had the embarrassment of having to bare my bum and get a tetanus injection because I had stood on a nail.

We stayed overnight in the Pennington Migrant Hostel. As we arrived in the dark I had no idea of where we were in the place, no clock to wake us for our early morning flight to Melbourne. When we woke and made our way to the reception area, I was frantically asking the time and realised we had missed our plane. I was really in a panic then as I had never missed a flight before but they just said, "don't worry we will get you another one". Finally, we arrived in Melbourne and my uncle was there to meet us. My aunty was horrified that I wasn't wearing a bra but that was the least of my concerns. We had gathered up a suitcase of clothes that we found at the Nakara house, but they were all covered in red mud so my uncle washed them off with the hose and he said that a worm came out of the dirt. Long trip for that worm!

Paul and I moved into a flat in Box Hill with whatever my relations could give us to use. We had mattresses on the floor for sleeping. Paul went to Box Hill Primary School and I used to walk him there every morning. Often I would walk on to spend time with my aunty. It was a pretty disjointed and lonely time for us. But one good thing came of it - we got help for Paul's dyslexia through an organisation called A New Start for the Under Achiever [ANSUA]. They assessed him and we started doing a motor sensory program. The aim was to re-pattern his brain so that he would know right from left. Apparently when babies crawl they are patterning their brain by doing opposite hand and leg movements and developing their sensory perception through contact with the surfaces that they crawl on.

Paul didn't really crawl much and unusually he couldn't cross the midline of his body, so he could march using the same hand and foot, which most people find hard to do. He even did it swimming at first but eventually was trained to swim properly with the Nightcliff Swimming Club. It was a hard time for him, as I had to make him crawl on his hands and knees every day as well as do other exercises.

CHAPTER 7

Post Cyclone Life and the Birth of Ashley

David came for a visit while we were in Melbourne and that's when I got pregnant with my son Ashley. We couldn't return to Darwin, without a special permit, which we didn't get until May 1975. Then we lived in David's old room in his parents' house at Bayview Street until we were allocated a caravan, which we put on their block in the garden. Paul went back to Darwin Primary School, which didn't sustain much damage in the cyclone.

My brother-in-law and his wife Val and their son Michael were living in what was my sister-in-law Joan's house — an annex of the main house where Joan now lived. Granny and Grandpa were still operating their service station in Nightcliff as it hadn't been too damaged in the cyclone.

We were living in the van when Ashley was born. It was a Saturday when I went into labour and David was playing first grade footy with the Waratahs so of course he had to go. Luckily for me, Val was home to help but we didn't have a phone so Val called the hospital from a phone box and then she took me to the hospital. Ashley was born at exactly 5 pm in the maternity ward at the old Darwin Hospital where I had worked for a while when I was nursing. David finally came to see me and, instead of him getting my story of the birth, I got a blow-by blow description of the footy game!

It was tough in the van with a newborn. David had to work and Paul had to go to school so if Ashley cried in the night, I would take him outside and walk around the yard. I started out breast-feeding him but I had not been able to do that with Paul, so it was all new to me. It was hard to get comfortable in the van and in the end I got mastitis and not long after that I put him on the bottle. I was very disappointed with myself but it was easier for all of us.

At the end of the footy season, the Waratahs had an overseas trip to Singapore and David felt quite comfortable to go off on that. I guess he thought it was OK because his mother and father were around. I was quite able to cope but deeply resented that the footy took precedence over his family. I guess he just wasn't ready for fatherhood.

At the time of the cyclone we were in the process of buying the house in Nakara. We were going to pay the deposit between Christmas and New Year but of course that didn't happen. That left us in limbo for a while and then we were told that people who had made offers to buy could go ahead and purchase the land. They even mistakenly bulldozed what was left for us thinking, it was still a government owned-block, which saved us some money. We were able to also get cheap finance through the government to rebuild. After the cyclone, everyone built at ground level so many years elapsed before we saw any elevated houses built.

Eventually our house was constructed and we finally left the caravan. I swore that I would never go in one again. The government had cleared the debris from blocks where they still owned the land and put demountable units on them for people to rent. They were still around and in use two to three years after the cyclone.

There was a couple with two young children living in a demountable two doors down from our house. We had heard them arguing a lot as sound travels in the Darwin open environment. The woman had one day asked me if she could use our phone so I knew what she looked like. Our house was built in a U-shape with a courtyard in the middle. One night, at about 1 am I heard a woman in our courtyard calling for help. I went to the glass door and was about to open it when I saw a man with a rifle. I called out to my husband and yelled that I was calling the police in the hope that the man would back off.

While I was on the phone I heard a shot so I told the police that I thought someone had been shot in our yard. I then went to look and found the woman on the ground. I could see that she had a wound in her arm but she kept telling me that she couldn't breathe. Naturally you tell the person that they are going to be OK and fortunately the police and the ambulance arrived quickly and took charge. I later learned that the man had shot her in the demountable, probably in the arm and she ran to our house for help, knowing that we had a telephone. The one shot that I heard had hit her in the lung, which was why she was telling me that she couldn't breathe. The woman survived and her partner was charged with attempted murder and we had to attend the trial as witnesses. He was sent to jail for about five years.

Another woman knocked on our door at night for help. She had accepted a lift home from a man that she knew but he headed for the beach instead. She was able to get out of the car but was stranded, hence the knock on our door. My husband knew her so he drove her home. We had a robbery where a pillowslip and a full set of my clothes including shoes was all that was stolen. Then there were the strange phone calls. On one call the caller said, "We are a couple who like to make a threesome and we think about you often", at which point I hung up. I fully expected that there would be more and then I would report it to the police but there were none until almost a year later. Same voice, but this time more explicit about what he and his wife wanted to do. I was sure that it was a particular neighbour, but could not prove that, of course. However, some time later I learned that his wife had left him and he was found guilty of sexual harassment at work, so my guess was probably correct. It was a weird time in Darwin for a while after the cyclone.

We had an above-ground pool and one day I had taken Ashley, who was only eighteen months old, in for a dip in the morning and then put him down for a nap. I asked David to remove the ladder. When Ashley woke up I took him with me out into the garden. I was digging away and heard a splash and thought, that little devil, he has thrown a stone in the pool. When I looked in, it wasn't a rock, it was him and the splash I heard was his hand breaking the water. I was able to lean in and grab him out but he was not breathing. Our neighbour Wayne heard me calling for help and jumped the fence and started to help me resuscitate him. I think it was his wife who called the ambulance because suddenly they were there. By that time we had him breathing so they just checked him out.

What had happened was that David didn't take the ladder away and several hours later when I went outside, I probably walked past the ladder but didn't notice it was still there because I had expected that it had been removed. After that incident, I took Ashley to Nightcliff pool to learn to swim classes for toddlers. I had to push him under the water to the instructor and I remember the first day I cried but I knew that I had to do it. He very quickly learnt to flop in from the side and turn around and get back to the side. That was how Paul got involved in the swimming club. This was great for him socially and for his co-ordination and he became a good swimmer. I used to time keep at the swimming carnivals and I still remember the day he won the backstroke at an interclub carnival.

CHAPTER 8

Marriage Breakdown and Moving to Canberra

A lot of marriages didn't survive the cyclone. It is amazing that ours did until 1980. We were really not suited to each other. There was the age difference and David as the youngest in the family had been spoilt and had never had to be responsible for much. I was the oldest who had been responsible for others. Now I wanted more out of life than I was getting. I might not have taken any direct action but in late 1979 while I was on a bus with the two boys going to an Alice Springs swimming carnival, I suddenly realised that David was having an affair. It was like a light had switched on in my head. We tried counselling but it didn't work.

I felt that Darwin was too small for me to stay, so in the summer of 1980 I packed up and took the boys to Canberra. I knew some people there who helped me to get a temporary job in the public service. I had applied for jobs in private enterprise but they always focused on what I would do if my kids were sick and I always missed out.

The job was with the CES in Belconnen and we were living in Mawson in a flat in a big complex, referred to as the Great Wall of China. Paul went to Torrens Primary School in Grade Six which was within walking distance. I found a family day care place for Ashley, the first one didn't work out but the next one was Sylvia Le Mesurier and he loved her and she loved him. She had two adopted children and one of her own, the youngest, Catherine, who Ashley went to preschool with.

Sylvia was so good to us. She didn't watch the clock like the other woman and one night a week she made dinner early and Ashley got fed too. He loved her cooking. It was a great relief to me to leave him with someone like her. It was tough though, dragging him out of bed so early and walking him to Sylvia's place, before I would run and catch the bus. It was so much easier when I got a car. I had no idea how to get to Belconnen except to follow the bus route, which I did till my confidence built up, then I took the Parkway.

Before I got the car I had to go to a parent- teacher night at Torrens Primary. I left the boys in the flat and set out to walk there by taking a short cut down the slope to the bike path. There was a car parked overlooking the path and the lights went on illuminating me. I just kept going, thinking nothing of it until I realised they had driven around the street and down the slope and were coming behind me on the path. I started to run but had stockings and slip-on sandals on my feet and I didn't seem to be going fast enough. I was just about to ditch my shoes when they stopped and I reached the road. When I got to the school I was so white in the face that people I had never met before asked me what had happened. They arranged for me to get a lift home after the meeting. I never did anything so foolish again. Probably no real harm was meant; they just wanted to scare me and they certainly achieved that.

I eventually got a permanent job in the CES and quickly achieved promotion to Employment Officer. By then I was working in the Civic office and then went to work with the Regional Director, organising staff for the whole of the CES in the ACT, including Queanbeyan.

CHAPTER 9

Returning to Darwin

It was a lonely life for us in Canberra and I wanted my boys to be near to their Fong family in Darwin, especially Granny, so I arranged a transfer back to Darwin. We first moved into a unit on Progress Drive in Nightcliff. Then we were allocated a Housing Commission house on Vanderlin Drive. We moved into it, although I was on the waiting list for a government house, it was uncertain that we would get one. Eventually we did and moved into the elevated house in Gsell St, Wanguri.

Paul was going to nearby Dripstone High School. Ashley continued on at Nightcliff Primary and attended after-school care there. Paul was playing hockey and Ashley was doing karate with his cousins Michael and Peter as well as playing cricket. David was living with someone and he took the kids for visits or a meal. Unfortunately, she didn't like me being around and made it impossible for me to get any help from David if either of the boys were sick. It was hard for me to bear the burden of taking all of the days off, but I did. Ashley sailed through school and finished Year Twelve just as he turned seventeen but for Paul school was a nightmare.

I had yet to find happiness in a relationship and continued to think that was something that I needed in my life. Plenty of guys wanted to have an affair with me but none were prepared to commit to a woman with two kids. I was pretty emotionally immature and I am not proud of that. I even felt that I needed to go on an overseas trip before I got too much older. As a teenager I read so many books and saw movies about the holocaust, so I wanted to go to Israel. If I was going that far I decided to see the Greek Islands as well. I arranged for a friend, Wayne, to stay with Paul in our house and for Ash to stay with a friend's mother, Karen.

I went overseas in May 1985. There had been a cyclone, Gretel, the first since Cyclone Tracy. The damage was mainly to trees and some property but it wasn't major. As it turned out, Wayne, who was an insurance assessor spent a lot of time down the track assessing cyclone damage for insurance claims so Paul who was only seventeen was left alone a lot. Although I thought that Ashley was OK being with his friends, I realised later how he must have been affected by my going away. Karen told me that although when I wrote to him I included Karen and her family in my letters he just kept them to himself. I still have the birthday card that he sent to me in Greece, which I didn't get at the time, but months later it turned up in Darwin.

When I think back to this time I am seriously remorseful that I was so hell-bent on pursuing my own needs. I was their mother and I should have been there for them no matter what my needs were. I am just so grateful for the strength of the relationship that I have with them both now and for all of the love they have shown me.

CHAPTER 10

My Overseas Adventure

Just before I went on my trip I started working with Clive. Clive had spent two years travelling overseas and he had been to Israel so we had that interest in common. When I was about to head off on my overseas trip he used to tease me that I would meet an Israeli tank commander. He liked me and was concerned that I had not found a partner. He warned me about travelling alone in the Middle East as a single woman. He scared the hell out of me with a story about western women who disappeared to supposedly turn up in harems in Saudi Arabia.

Fortunately I survived my trip but I did have some interesting experiences. In Egypt I contracted the dreaded Tutankhamen's Curse and was laid up in my hotel with dreadful vomiting and diarrhoea. The doctor came and treated me and when he gave me an injection in the buttock he seemed to spend a long time massaging me before and after the injection. I dismissed this as I was obviously in a very unattractive condition. However later that evening he rang and asked me if I needed any more "service". It was a first for me to get the offer of such personal attention from a medical professional.

When I arrived in Tel Aviv I went for a walk and a young Israeli man came up and made conversation. He was very pleasant and we had an interesting chat about a range of things. As I said goodbye to head back to the hotel he asked me if I would like to go to bed with him. I knew Israelis had a reputation for not beating about the bush but I was still a little taken aback. I pointed out that I was nearly old enough to be his mother and found his approach a little direct. He then very kindly pointed out that I was a bit too friendly and would need to be careful. I took on board his advice and was reminded of Clive's warnings.

I was forty and unattached so I guess it was inevitable that I would have one romantic adventure. His name was Aaron and I met him on the first part of my trip in Israel. I went on a tour to Egypt and Jordan and had to return across the Allenby Bridge in Jordan. Aaron told me he would meet me on the Israeli side of the border. It was an adventurous part of the journey and a little traumatic so I was very relieved and impressed when he turned up. I think it had such an impact because I had been let down by men a lot in my life.

Clive's smug prediction that I would meet an Israeli tank commander turned out to be wrong although he was an Army reserve officer (nearly everyone in Israel is a reservist) so I guess he was not that far wrong. He was an interesting and intelligent man who had travelled a lot in Europe and in retrospect I concluded that he probably worked for Israeli intelligence.

He gave me the name Sara Leah and treated me to a wonderful time showing me the Israel beneath the organised tours. We did correspond for a while and he encouraged me to be open to a future relationship as he could see I had been let down previously. He tried to convince me that men were not all unreliable.

It was a good lesson as soon after in my life would be Clive who proved to be the most decent and reliable man imaginable. I even gave Clive an Israeli nickname - Moshe.

Before leaving Darwin I had an on-and-off relationship with a man who could not commit. That relationship was an emotional roller-coaster ride for me and once again something that I am not proud of. He wouldn't make a commitment and yet wouldn't let go, even to the point of finding out my overseas itinerary and turning up at Athens airport when I arrived from Israel.

He convinced me to come to England with him to meet his family and we travelled together for a couple of weeks. It never felt right and as I was leaving from London airport he said it was all over again. That was finally it for me.

It had been a wonderful and adventuress trip but it ended on a sour note and I think I made a decision that I would be better off on my own for a while. Little did I know what lay ahead.

CHAPTER 11

Clive comes into my Life

C live and I had been working together in the corporate services area of the Department of Employment in Darwin. He was the training manager and I had to liaise with him on managing resources.

In 1986, we both got promoted as managers in the Corporate Services area and so worked even more closely together and went to the same management meetings. We were always at each other about something and one of the women in the office said we squabbled like a married couple. That was prophetic.

Clive came to the Territory in 1983. We had returned the previous year and I was working at the Casuarina CES. He came to be the new Training Manager and I first met him in the tearoom at Casuarina when he came on a tour of all of our offices. He had a very bushy beard and was dressed in grey trousers and shirt. After he left, I being a smarty said to the people, "Who was that garden gnome"? He found out that I said that and to this day has not revealed who told him! It's hard now to remember the sequence of events but I got to know him and like him, and even baby-sat for him and his wife once at my suggestion. I eventually moved from the CES into the Regional Office in town where Clive also worked. So we got to know each other even better.

At some point Clive recruited Paul Nixon (Nico) to the Training Section, and, boy, were they a pair of rascals. When they recruited a young woman, Gerri Alver, to the section they were a very fun group as well as being very good trainers. Both Paul and Gerri have remained close friends throughout my life.

In October 1986, Clive and I went on a one-week management course at Kakadu. On a residential course you are in an unnatural environment, that is, you are away from work and your home responsibilities. You do a lot of activities in groups and socialising at night, which breaks down barriers. I had always thought of Clive as a dear friend and good work-mate, also as the quintessential married man and father. So I didn't feel any need to guard myself from him although I had thought that he was the type of man I would like in my life.

Over the course of the week our, good friends' relationship developed into a love affair. I thought that it was a flash in the pan on his part, never realising the integrity of the man he was. While he didn't want to desert his kids he saw me as the love of his life and wanted to be with me. I said he should go to counselling with his wife expecting that would be the end of it but the outcome was that they separated and not amicably. The counselling identified to Clive that the marriage had been in serious trouble for a long time.

CHAPTER 12

The Testing of a Relationship

Clive was very courageous to make such a move as Lisa was not yet four and there was a very acrimonious custody battle and divorce settlement. We also got paid out at work, which was none of anybody else's business but they made it so, to the point where senior management let their feelings about us affect our careers. At around the same time senior management had been running a scam where they would have lunches at the topless waitress bar in Parap with selected staff members and charge it to the training budget of the Department. One of Clive's staff in the Accounts Section drew the invoices to his attention. The invoices came from a business called Red Tower, which was a company set up by one of the senior managers purely for the purpose of spending Commonwealth funds illegally.

Clive and a friend, Andrew Bray, got all of the paper-work together and sent it to the Secretary of the Department. When nothing was done about it they wrote to the Minister anonymously. Meanwhile Clive had swapped jobs with a woman in Customs and I had transferred to the Department of Defence, after lodging a complaint about how senior management had treated me professionally. Eventually the Department agreed that I had not been afforded my rights, which was some comfort but all too late.

Somehow Clive was asked to see Senator Bob Collins, a cabinet minister in Canberra, as John Dawkins, the Minister for Education and Employment, had asked Bob if he knew anything about Clive. Clive explained the whole story to Bob who rang Dawkins and vouched for him including that he was a member of the Labor Party in the NT. Unfortunately, Dawkins wrote on the papers that the officer was in Customs and sent the papers to the Departmental Secretary for an investigation, which they could not ignore. From that they were able to identify Clive and we bore the brunt of the local managers' anger.

When they sent an investigation team to Darwin they started to investigate us first. They came to our house in Wanguri on a Sunday and questioned us about the house. I was the Resources Manager, responsible for the maintenance program on the houses the department had. So they questioned things like our verandah upgrade, but I was able to show them that it was a program of maintenance that had been drawn up independently of me.

Clive and I had a three months transfer to Canberra prior to all of this. We had in mind that we might transfer there but he would have left his kids behind and there were my two boys to consider so in the end we ruled it out. The investigation team questioned whether we had abused the Travel Allowance [TA] system while in Canberra. That was also unfounded, due to Clive insisting that when I joined him in Canberra that they only paid me for meals, whereas in the first three weeks I was entitled to the full TA with no requirement for acquitting the expenses. Even if I had accepted the full TA I would not have broken any rules but we had done what Clive thought was the correct thing.

Then one of the guys under investigation said that because we owned a flat that we weren't entitled to government housing. That didn't get any traction either because the housing policy said that 'you weren't entitled if it was accommodation that you could be reasonably expected to live in' and of course we couldn't live in a two-bedroom unit with four kids.

One of Clive's best friends was involved in the scam and he had already given us a hard time about our relationship so after his formal reprimand over what came to be called "Red Tower" he blamed us. He even went so far as to malign me to an interview panel when I went for a job in Centrelink which would have been a promotion. I didn't manage to get promoted to that level until after I came back from China ten years later. If I had been promoted to the Centrelink job back in 1990 it would have made a big difference to my super. I had named him in my official complaint so he hated me for that and it was hatred, for both Clive and me. It was easier to see us as the cause of his shame, rather than accept that he had brought himself down with his own actions. It was an awful time for us but somehow we survived it.

We were fortunate that at both Customs and Defence we had supportive supervisors. As long as we were performing our jobs well they had no issue with us. Clive built a good career for himself in Customs going from the Corporate Services job to various operational areas, including working overtime at the airport, processing incoming international flights.

I stayed with Defence for four years and had a very interesting time. My main job was to manage the twenty-five office staff that provided all of the Corporate Services functions relating to the civilians employed at the Army, Navy and RAAF bases in the NT.

During my tenure there I was involved in two unique events. The first was a military exercise with the Americans and Asian countries called "Kangaroo 89". It was held in the dry season of 1989 and was the biggest military exercise in Australia since WWII. There were thousands of additional military personnel to be accommodated and fed which meant that we had to recruit additional civilian staff. The town of Darwin was buzzing and it was a thrilling time to be working in Defence.

The Defence Department finally realised that they needed to recognize the "Black Diggers" from WWII for their service to the country. This involved identifying them or, if they had died, their relatives, working out what wages they would have been entitled to had they been properly enlisted and converting it to current value. There were two groups, one from the Tiwi Islands and one from Arnhem Land. The, Diggers, who were still alive and a family representative for the others were brought to Darwin for an official recognition ceremony. There was a smoking ceremony and they did the dance that depicts the bombing of the Tiwi Islands by the Japanese. I remember this old Tiwi Digger holding my hand and thanking me for the recognition. It was a proud moment for me.

My boss was on leave so I was in charge when the war

with Iraq broke out and as Australia was part of it we had to go on alert even though we were nowhere near the action. That was the nearest that I ever got to a real war!

I even got to go in an F18 simulator at Tindal air base near Katherine which was an amazing experience. I took the top off the tower in Martin Place, Sydney, but managed to land without going off the runway but I think there was someone manipulating my success. My boss was annoyed because he had never been offered a go. I went home and said to Clive we had to rent the movie *Top Gun* which we had never seen so I could relive my high flying experience.

I had one other interesting experience, more like bizarre actually. I had a visit from mysterious man who put the Official Secrets Act on my desk but didn't say anything about it. Then he proceeded to tell me that he needed me to play a role in a secret operation. If I got a call asking for a certain person (who wasn't working at Defence) I was to say that they were out of the office. I must have performed my role OK but as a "spy" I was completely in the dark.

I knew that I had had the best out of my time in Defence and it was time to move on so I applied for a transfer to Immigration. Like Clive did with Customs I went first into a Corporate Service Manager's job and later transferred to various program delivery sections including working at the airport.

The good thing about the move to Immigration was that Clive and I did have some professional interaction. As I mentioned earlier we had always had similar values and work ethic so it was interesting to be in that situation again on occasion.

We worked together very closely at the airport managing international flight arrivals and although this was mostly routine we did have to deal with some interesting situations. One night we had the Pakistani Prime Minister's plane arrive in Darwin to refuel on the way back from CHOGM in New Zealand. When the plane went to take off a piece broke off the engine and pierced the fuel tank creating a very dangerous situation. The Prime Minister and all his staff ended up back in our outwards lounge while awaiting the arrival of a replacement aircraft. It was great fun talking to the group about all sorts of things and they were big admirers of Shane Warne, "a very fine leg-spinner". They were getting very hungry by 2 am and nothing was open so Clive arranged for some food to be brought back from the stricken plane. This was of course contrary to quarantine regulations as officially the food on the plane had been cleared out of the country. As it turned out we obtained a large tub of ice-cream and found a place away from the prying eyes of the quarantine people. I found some spoons in the kitchen and the Prime Minister and his staff ate directly from the tub. They all thought it was very amusing and even sent a thank you note to us some weeks later.

One morning after working an early shift we came home to a very funny event. Milo, our dog, was a rascal and nervy besides. He would always get up to mischief when Clive and I worked at the airport for the 4 am starts to do the Customs and Immigration clearances. One morning we came home and I said to Clive, "What are all those rubber bands doing in the breezeway?" On closer inspection we saw that they were condoms. Milo used to sneak in and sleep on David's bed and he had found his condom supply and ripped the packets open. I left dealing with that one to Clive. The final word came from Gumby, Clive's Customs mate, he said "That's one smart dog, because I can never get those things open".

We had another interesting event where we co-operated in achieving an outcome. In the mid-nineties we were getting Sino-Vietnamese refugees arriving in Darwin and Clive and I were both involved in the interception and processing of these people. There was a Chinese junk that arrived with about forty people on board. The vessel was actually a very interesting example of a traditional wooden junk and the Northern Territory Maritime Museum was keen to get a hold of it. Unfortunately there was a complicated legal process that meant the boats had to be maintained on the water for months and by then were usually in such a bad state that they were brought ashore and burned.

Clive and I were good friends with Nigel Scullion who ran the company that was contracted to manage the boats seized by the Commonwealth. We hatched a plan to get the boat out of the water at the Museum, which is located right on the beach in Darwin, and donate it. Clive and Nigel sailed the boat around to the ramp and a crane placed it in the courtyard of the museum where it remains today as a unique exhibit.

Unfortunately, the next week, Clive was contacted by the lawyer for the refugees, asking for the boat back.

Apparently the people wanted to sail away as it looked like they would not be given refugee status. I guess they were planning to go to New Zealand. This did cause us a bit of a panic as once these old wooden boats are out of the water they shrink and leak. However it was a legal bluff, so we held our nerve and said we would make the boat available if needed. It was a risk but we did not suffer any consequences.

The three of us had a great laugh about the event. Nigel and his wife attended our wedding in 1996. Nigel of course went on to become a Senator for the Northern Territory and shadow minister in the Liberal National Party.

The highlight of my time in Immigration was successfully winning a posting to China, which is a topic for a later chapter.

CHAPTER 13

Building a Blended Family

Clive's kids were coming to us on Thursday one week and the next week from Thursday to Sunday. We were still in the Wanguri house and Paul very quickly tired of having his space invaded by three little kids so often. We were cramped for space with just three small bedrooms and only one small bathroom. So Paul moved out and went to share with his cousin Christopher.

I didn't think it was ideal so we scraped together $9,000 to put a deposit on a two bedroom unit in Malak and Paul moved in there. Ashley was king of the kids as it was his house and he owned all of the toys. Carl and David idolised him. Poor Lisa, she now had three boys to cope with. It was hard for me with her because I had raised two boys and didn't know much about little girls and we didn't have any toys for girls to start out.

After Clive came to live with us, Ashley got the dog he had wanted for some time. I knew that on my own it was something else to look after and I couldn't afford veterinary fees if it got sick. We went out to the pound with the four kids and we wandered about looking at all of the dogs and finally Clive pointed out a big white dog. All of the others had jumped up looking for attention but not this one. So we got him and he was named Bouncer after some dog on TV, I think in "*Home and Away*".

Bouncer wasn't very smart but a good dog and we all liked him. He started out as an outside dog but after a 4 am call from the neighbour, complaining about his barking, I hauled him inside to our bedroom so I could shush him up if he barked as no one else ever heard him at night. We have some video footage taken by Carl of Clive trying to get him to heel, which is quite funny. He could never sit straight.

We had a plague of nits for months. Every weekend when Carl, David and Lisa arrived, they had nits. It was the first time I had seen hatched ones. I only ever saw eggs on my two boys. I didn't like to inspect their hair the minute that they walked in the door but sure enough the next day I would find them and off we would go with the treatment. I thought I would go crazy. Once I even had to cut Lisa's long hair quite short. We couldn't get the nits out of her long hair and no hairdresser would cut her hair while she was infested. Eventually the plague stopped and we had no more trouble with nits again.

I tried to impress standards on Carl, David and Lisa that they weren't used to and that caused conflict between Clive and me. We went to a counsellor to help us sort out what was reasonable in the circumstances. It was tough going because at this time Leonie wasn't in a good frame of mind towards us. I look back to that time now and wonder how we all made it through to be the family that we are today.

We purchased the house in Wanguri and, not too long after, we sold it to move to something a bit larger. That was when we purchased the Troppo designed house in Leanyer. It was a very different house but Clive and I were very attracted to how much cooler it was and that it also had a pool, which we had had at Wanguri. It was very open with very little in the way of noise barriers. Ashley would not even come and have a look at it before we moved in. When we moved in he complained that it was like camping and that he had a cricket in his room so he couldn't sleep there. I realise now that he didn't want to be taken out of his comfort zone. However we all adapted to it in the end.

I had met Clives' mother and she was very welcoming despite my apprehensions. The first year I went to Portarlington in Victoria to visit at Christmas her husband Keith was in the final stages of cancer.

Ede was distraught so when I looked after Keith at home for a few days Ede decided I was a wonderful partner for Clive. Ede used to come to visit and when she married Jack they both came up. In 1991 we took them on a trip to Europe and America and we were glad that we had because about a year later Ede was diagnosed with kidney cancer and she died in November 1993. Not too long after we found out about Ede's illness, my father was diagnosed with Motor Neurone Disease.

We had some good trips with all of the kids at different times. We took Paul and Ashley on our trip to Tioman Island and Singapore but they weren't so keen on white sandy beaches; they wanted to shop. One good outcome was that we met our French friends, Jacques and Jacqueline, and later visited them in France and they also came to visit us in Darwin.

That was the trip where we sent my two boys ahead of us to Singapore. I knew that Paul would watch over

Ashley and that Ash would make sure he didn't get robbed changing money. By the time we got there Ash had worked out where the best value money change place was. I always say that he was born counting. He certainly didn't get his mathematical ability from me.

We did quite a few trips to Bali with various combinations of the kids. It was on one of those trips with Ash and David where we met Mark and Joan (see the chapter on the Americans). They are a truly inspirational couple. It would not have been possible to do so much travel if it hadn't been for Paul always being prepared to come back and mind the dogs and the house.

For about eighteen months Clive and I extended every business trip we had down south to help out with Ede and Dad. We still had to manage our jobs and Clive had responsibilities with his kids. Ash was still living at home doing a gap year before going to university. Despite the history I had with my father I hated to see him suffer. Even Mum ran her own health down by tending him at home. He wouldn't go near the GP so Mum or I would talk to him about changes in symptoms. I wrote Dad long letters, sometimes more than one a week, to give him something to look forward to. I wrote to Mum to bolster her spirits. I know that underneath I was searching to find if my father really loved me. I thought that he had only written me one note in all that time, but recently while sorting through photos and papers I found a card where he said "I love you".

My father died in January 1994 just before Ash was to head off to Canberra and ANU. I remember not long after I came back from his funeral, Ash must have been mad at me about something and he told me that when I got old he would put me in a home. I went off and had a cry and Clive came and said that of course he didn't mean it. I knew that too, but I was still a bit fragile and worried about my mother who wasn't in really good shape. I was probably worried about Ashley going on his own to live in Canberra too.

Mum's health continued to be bad. She had a back problem that nothing could be done about. Fortunately she had two sisters and their husbands who were close by. Eventually she needed to go into an assisted-living facility but there wasn't a place in the one in Wonthaggi. We got her into a new facility in Tarcutta where Brian lived and she was there for only three months when she was diagnosed with aggressive lung cancer and needed high care. So Brian and I got her back to Wonthaggi into the nursing home there.

I remember leaving Mum and Brian in the car and going in to meet the Matron and bursting into tears. Anyone who has done that with a parent will know the feeling. Mum died in May 1995. Her dreams of having a life of her own after Dad, were gone. I think in the end they were so bound by their antagonism that she was lost without it.

My elocution lessons were put to good use when my parents died. We were not religious and so we decided on a graveside service for Dad which I wrote and delivered. My elocution teacher, Mrs Arthur, attended Dad's funeral and she commented on what a good job I did. Mum asked for the same so I did hers too. We used the same funeral director each time and he asked me if I would like a job. If I had been living in Wonthaggi I might have taken his offer up as it is important for families that funerals are done right.

It was also around this time that Clive and I got involved in politics. The Northern Territory was a place for cowboy politicians and the ruling Country Liberal Party(CLP) had been in power for many years.

When the CLP member for Wanguri died suddenly, there was a by-election called and it was a fait-accomplit, that the CLP would win as they held the seat with 65% of the vote. However they pre-selected a candidate who was the football coach of St Mary's and a work colleague of mine. They assumed because he was well known and a real blokes' bloke that he would win easily. I did not believe that he was a worthy candidate at all and got all fired up and went to the local Australian Labor party (ALP) branch to see if we could help out.

Clive and I just about doubled the attendance as there were no ALP sitting members in the northern suburbs of Darwin and it was seen as a hopeless task to try and win the seat. We met John Bailey the ALP candidate who was a decent man, a former teacher and practising psychologist and certainly a much more suitable person to enter politics. I was a Wonthaggi girl where the miners union was ever present so my allegiance had always been to the party representing working people.

In any case we threw ourselves into the task and the electorate was so small that it was possible to door-knock every house during the by-election. We knew the CLP guy would be exposed under scrutiny because it was a by-election and that proved to be the case.

We won the election and John Bailey became the local member and stayed in politics for many years before becoming mayor. Clive and I stayed members for about eight years and were fortunate to meet people like Bob Hawke, John Dawkins and Kim Beazley as the ALP held power federally. The highlight for me was meeting Paul Keating after he became Prime Minister and he was by far the most impressive person I have ever met. He was charming, intelligent and very personable face-to-face. It was always a mystery to me why so many people disliked him so much because in my view he was the most visionary PM in Australia since WW II.

Like all things the gloss started to wear off as we became embroiled in all the petty faction stuff that is a feature of the ALP. Clive and I were asked what faction did we want to join and we said we were both quite happy just doing our thing in the Wanguri Branch. We were told that was politically naive to which Clive responded that he happened to be president of the ONLY branch in Darwin with a sitting member so he did not appreciate being lectured to about how to succeed in politics.

It was around this time that Bob Collins (the Federal Senator) and John Bailey sounded me out about running for a local seat. There was a push to change the party and in particular get more women as candidates. I was horrified about the prospect of entering politics despite Clives' encouragement that I would do well. I honestly could never have handled the scrutiny especially with my colourful past. In retrospect I guess it was a bit of feather in my cap to be asked but I have no regrets at all.

I was reminded of all this recently when visiting Darwin in July to see Paul and Clive and I ran into John Bailey who was thrilled to see us both and naturally a little shocked that I had MND and could no longer speak.

CHAPTER 14

The Americans and One German

Travel has been a highlight of my life and with that comes encounters with interesting people.

Clive has always been more open than me to meeting new people and maintaining friendships. He puts time and effort into it and thanks to his work I have also benefited from those friendships. In the seventies Clive travelled in South America as part of more than two years travelling with his former wife, Leonie. It was there that he met three guys from California, Brad, Preston and Robert, who were all from Mariposa near Yosemite National Park.

In 1991 on a trip to America we met up with Preston's sister Alison who was married to Robert's brother, John. They had a fantastic house on property outside of Mariposa with a creek running through it where we all used to cool off in the summer. We also met Brad's wife Gail and they were living in a place called Willits in Northern California. They would come to the "Ranch" as Alison and John's place was called along with Preston and we would have the greatest times around the island bench in their kitchen. The girls were great at cooking Mexican food and making salsa to go with the ever flowing margaritas that John would make. Margaritas never taste as good anywhere else. I think they were just part of the lovely times we all shared.

It was Brad and Gail who had Lisa to stay with them for three months and she went to the local school with their two children, Callen and Alyssa. Gail was the school nurse. Lisa had a wonderful time. Our kids all visit both families whenever they are in the States. Gail and a friend came to visit us in China and Brad and Gail and John and Alison have been to visit us in Narooma.

Another special relationship with two Americans began in Bali in 1989 when we met Mark and Joan Reiss. We had Ashley and David with us on that trip and we stayed in a little fishing village called Padang Bai in Western Bali. It was a beautiful and simple place, relatively untouched by tourism at that time. Clive had noticed this very fit-looking couple jogging in the morning and struck up a conversation. A day or so later he convinced Mark to sublet his hire car for a day so we could take the boys on a trip to the nearby volcano. That meeting was the start of a fascinating friendship that has lasted over twenty years.

On the face of it we didn't have much in common. They were older than us by ten to fifteen years. Clive and I were just two-mid level public servants while Mark and Joan were serious achievers. Mark was a Radiologist and accomplished pianist who had had to make a decision to pursue medicine or a career as a concert pianist. Joan was an extraordinary achiever who done everything from standing for Congress to running across Death Valley. She has also personally met Robert Redford and Arnold Schwarzenegger and the stories attached to those meetings are really something. Nevertheless we two couples clicked and despite living on different continents we have managed to meet up regularly.

We have had some great adventures together. They visited us in Darwin and we took them on a hike in Nitmuluk National Park near Katherine. Hiking in the Northern Territory can be dangerous because of the remoteness and the heat. During the twenty kilometre trek on the first day we misjudged the amount of water that we needed. The first ten kilometres had been relatively easy with a spring where we could cool off. The next ten we were walking over rocks that were buried under trampled spear grass so you couldn't easily judge your footing. It wasn't helped by the poor marking of the track. We had used nearly all of our water and were still unsure of how much further we had to go to reach our objective which was Crystal Falls. Mark and Clive decided that Clive should take the last of the water which happened to be Mark's and go on to locate the falls. As it turned out they were only around the next bend and we all floundered into the gorgeous water and drank our fill. We pitched our tents, ate and slept like babies.

The next morning we had this magnificent place all to ourselves and, lo and behold, our American friends present themselves for the day "starkers" to swim and sun-bathe. Clive and I saw this as a subtle challenge to the Australian character so we discarded our bathers and all had a fun day "au natural".

When we visited them in California in 1991 to see them for the first time since we met in Bali, they were in the process of renovating a house that they had bought in San Francisco. It was situated on the steepest street that I had ever seen, but with fabulous views. Mark and Joan had a trip to Alaska planned so after the first day they gave us the keys to the house and left us with the builders, to stay as long as we wanted. What trust they showed in us when they had probably only spent three days in total getting to know us.

We have a host of amazing stories shared with Mark and Joan including the extraordinary year where they ran into Ashley at an extinct volcano in Costa Rica and then six months later into Carl at Angkor Wat in Cambodia. In both cases they had no idea that our kids were in the area. Mark and Joan grew up in New York so they still have their New York accents and the kids heard their voices before they saw them and guessed it was them. That's pretty incredible.

Our friendship with them has been a wonderful part of our lives. Clive and I attended their fiftieth wedding anniversary celebration and "roasted and toasted" them in front of their family and friends. They returned the favour in Australia at Clive's sixtieth birthday party. Our kids have all been welcome in their home at various times as they have grown up and gone travelling. Mark and Joan have always shown a keen interest in what our kids have been doing.

Since I was diagnosed with MND they have provided terrific support, albeit from afar, and made yet another trip from the USA to see me in Narooma. Clive and I treasure this unlikely and very special friendship.

There is one other special overseas relationship that began for me in 1985 on a plane between Jordan and Singapore. I sat next to a young man named Lars Engbert, who as it turned out was the same age as Paul, about 19. He offered me a Mars Bar and it went from there. I had a long stopover in Singapore and so I went with him and a German girl he was going to share lodgings with while they settled in. Then we had a meal together and I headed for the airport.

Lars and I corresponded for a long time. What was so unique was that he was corresponding with someone who was old enough to be his mother and somehow I think he saw me as another mother figure. We lost touch as you do but Clive located him for me and eventually he came to visit us in Darwin with his girlfriend. Once again we lost touch and yet again Clive tracked him down. We visited him when we were on our round-the-world trip in 1991. He was living with another girl by then near where her parents ran a farm. They are now married with three children. We caught up with Lars in Sydney a few years ago while he was on a work trip and he also met our German friend Juergen and they hit it off at once.

When Lars heard that I had MND he came to Narooma to visit me. He wanted me to come to Germany to see his doctor who he was convinced would heal me. Lars found it hard to accept that I could not be cured. He is a wonderful man, so enthusiastic for life, and we have been unlikely friends for twenty-eight years.

The front yard in Wonthaggi circa 1951.

I was chosen to present Miss Australia flowers at Darwin Hospital
(around 1966) Note I have then around the wrong way so it looks
like she is giving them to me.

Paul and I at Shady Camp with a Barra caught by David 1973.

Granny Fong with the kids after I returned to Darwin around 1982.

The house at Nakara a few days after Cyclone Tracy 1975.

Early photo with Clives children and Ash in Wanguri.

Clive loved this photo of me on our first trip to Bali 1988.

Clive and I are at the cricket watching Ashley (1990)

Clive and I on one of our first trips to Bali.

Our marriage on the Darwin Esplanade with Eileen West
and Rob Millen June 1996.

I had just had root canal treatment before this trip to Guilin China
on a break from the the work in Guangzhou.

Tom Calma and I in Hanoi where he was on posting in 2000.

On the ice with Rob and Wendy in Beijing 2001.

Dancing with Emma at her wedding in Narooma.

At Glasshouse Rocks with Milo 2008.

Clive and I with a catch at Glasshouse Rocks,
what a great hunting team we were.

Our Grand Design just after construction in 2007.

With Hannah and Max just before I was diagnosed.

One hundred feet up and going like a son of a gun.

With Harry B. and E.L.S. just before I was displaced.

CHAPTER 15

My Boys Moving on in the World

Paul managed to get work in information technology with the Department of Education. I could never understand him doing that or how he coped. But cope he did and even got a degree in it. He always had a good memory and he took in a lot of information by watching TV. When he was first looking for a job I had the psychologist at the CES do an aptitude test on him and he came out very strong on the ability to deal with people. He was so introverted then that he disavowed that assessment. Despite the struggle that he had at school he got a job and has always had one. He set about educating himself through part-time study and I am so proud of what he has achieved and I also recognise how hard a slog it has been. But he has two degrees and honours in one and soon he will be a qualified psychologist. No matter the path that he has taken to get there, I know that he will be a great psychologist.

When Ash left for ANU Paul came home to live to save some money after we sold the unit in Malak. Clive's son David was also living with us and at that stage we still had Bouncer and also Milo who we got when the neighbour's dog Toby had pups. Paul was still seriously introverted and some days would come home and walk straight past us in the kitchen and go into his room without any greeting.

I remember that I was always trying to make excuses to Clive for his unsociable behaviour. I understood that after working all day with people he was thoroughly drained. Not only that, he would have been doing administrative work that would have been putting him under pressure too. Dyslexia is a hidden disability and it is not easy to tell people that you have difficulties with reading and writing when you otherwise seem so intelligent. How he suffered with it all and yet has achieved so much.

I was at work at the airport one Saturday when Clive took Paul to look at units in Milner. The result was that he bought his unit, which was still in its original 1970s state. Mustard carpet and tortoise-shell laminate on all of the cupboards. The good thing was that it had been well built at the time and the basics like the sliding doors were still good. I remember one time when we were visiting I was sitting in the lounge and suddenly a pile of the kitchen tiles fell off the wall. I think that the adhesive and grout just gave out. He lived in it like that for a long time until he was ready to renovate and what a great job he did of it. Completely gutted the place and now it is unrecognisable, it is so modern and done in such good taste.

Paul has a close group of friends. He has worked hard to be less introverted and is a much more sociable person and has a good social life. He still gets very tired from work and needs down time to recover his mental energy but he well understands how to deal with these pressures now.

School was easy for Ashley and he did very well. I remember seeing him off to his Year Ten graduation in a stretch limousine with his friends, dressed in a tuxedo.

Clive and I went along to the presentation and I remember he was awarded a prize. He was a great junior cricketer and won so many trophies. We thought the cases of Coke were the best value though!

The most wonderful day was when he played in the Benson and Hedges Cup in the senior Nightcliff cricket team at Gardens Oval. It was a beautiful dry season day and to my shame Clive and I were on our way into town and thought we would just drop in for a quick look. Well, we stayed to the end. The other team thought that since he was just a kid and not a very big kid that they would get him out straight away. The first ball was a bouncer, which he had to duck. The next ball he whacked into the stand for a six and then hit some fours and at least one other six. At the end of the game, which Nightcliff won, Ash was named man of the match, the youngest and smallest player on the field. Many years later he revealed that these men he was playing against sledged him by asking him how long he had been off the boat,(a reference to his Asian appearance).That was his moment in the sun. Paul's was the day he won the backstroke in the interclub swimming competition. Each required a lot of determination. They both represented the NT in their sports but to me those were their standout events.

Except for his learning difficulties Paul was no trouble as a teenager, just introverted and hard to reach. Ash on the other hand, while not getting into drugs or fights, discovered girls in about Year Eleven. When he went out I always went and picked him up, whereas I hadn't had to do that with Paul. Ash said to me years later that I treated him as if he was a girl!

I was really put on the back foot when his girlfriend Naomi started staying over. I hadn't met her parents who lived out of town but I thought I was at least doing the right thing by having her sleep in the spare room. The next thing I discovered was that she had moved into Ashley's room because she was "scared". What to do, what to do? I remember asking Ash if he slept in Naomi's room on the odd occasion that he stayed at her place and he said yes. I was stripping the beds in his room on a Sunday morning when I found a pair of girl's underwear mixed up in the sheets. Well, I really had to do something then and I confronted them both. I can't remember what I said but I would have told Naomi that I was concerned about whether her parents knew that she was sexually active. I do know that later I talked to Ash about how differently girls looked at sex compared to boys and that they tended to have expectations that the boys might not want to meet. This proved to be the case when Naomi followed him to Canberra and it didn't work out the way that she had planned.

A few years later we went through the same situation again, this time with David, I couldn't believe it. He also had a girlfriend who lived out of town and they were both only sixteen. When we tried to talk to him he said that we had let Ashley do it. That wasn't quite right as we never felt comfortable with it, so I gave him the same talk about girls and their expectations. David had been living with us for quite awhile and he learnt eventually that I was right.

In his second year at ANU Ash met Emma. I remember that he put her on the phone to talk to me and I wondered what to say to a young girl that I had never met. We finally met her when we went to Canberra to celebrate Ashley's twenty-first birthday. We met her at a cricket match in which he was playing. Then he brought her up to Darwin for Christmas and the four of us went out to Kakadu. On the way back in torrential rain the windscreen wipers on the car broke. Emma thought it was so funny that I had my head out of the window trying to make sure we stayed on the road.

She stayed on with us when Ash went to Brisbane for work experience related to his studies. I guess that is where Emma, Clive and I formed the bond that is still with us today.

Granny Fong was a great example of inclusion and tolerance as she welcomed Clive's kids and treated them like grandchildren. She also did the same with an ex-boyfriend of her daughter Eli, who later married and used to take his wife and kids to see Granny. From her example I came to the conclusion that you can include whoever you want into your family, that it is not all about blood relatives.

I was travelling a lot to Canberra while Ash was at ANU and used to stay with him at Burton and Garran Hall. The first time he forgot to get the fold-up bed and I had to sleep on the floor. I think maybe he hadn't known how to say that it wasn't cool to have your mother come to stay. But I kept at it, as it was really the only way that I could spend time with him. I got to be a bit of a fixture wandering the halls in my pajamas to go to the bathroom.

Ash got a double degree in Economics and Commerce and I remember asking him why he wasn't going to do Honours and he said that he could earn more in a year working than the starting salary he would get with Honours. Six months before he finished university he had applied for and been successful in getting a job as a trader with Banker's Trust. I remember being shocked at the amount of his first year bonus. My son was working in a world that I could not understand but he has been both good at it and worked hard. He didn't take holidays for a few years while Banker's Trust was bought out by Deutsche Bank and finally by Macquarie Bank. Mergers are typically times when you can lose your job but he never has. In the mean-time he and Emma split up while she was still at university. Timing wasn't right and she is now married with three kids and Ashley is still a committed bachelor so the time was never going to be right.

Ash got a job working on a joint venture between Macquarie Bank and the Bank of Abu Dhabi. I found it hard to see him off to Dubai/Abu Dhabi but he had a great life there and Clive and I did get to visit and he showed us a great time. He took us to brunch at a hotel complex called El Quasar. It was the most amazing experience where about five restaurants opened out to a courtyard and provided the most amazing food. Just about everything you could think of as well as dishes cooked on demand. Only in the Emirates! We had a great side trip to Oman with him too.

When the offer of London came up he wasn't entirely ready to leave Dubai/Abu Dhabi but realised that there might not be another opportunity to go there so he accepted and moved to London. We only got to see him there when Clive and I went to see our friends Lydia and Doug in the Netherlands where Lydia was Australia's Ambassador to The Hague. We spent a weekend with him in London. On our last trip to America Ashley came over from London and we met up in my favourite city, which is New York.

All of our friends who have met my boys tell me what lovely men they are and I have to agree even though I am their mother. They both have good taste and present themselves well. Ashley has worn suits a lot because of his work and to friend's weddings. The only time Paul has ever worn a suit was at my brother Brian's wedding. I remember Lisa commenting after visiting Ash in Sydney that he used the same toothpaste and cleaning products that I did. I thought that was funny that she would notice that.

It is hard for a mother to let go and recognise that her sons are men with their own lives to live. I think that I took longer than most to do that; maybe that was a result of single parenting, I don't know. What I do know is that my two sons are my legacy in this world.

CHAPTER 16

Step Children Achieving

All of our children have gone to university and I have spoken about my two but not much about the achievements of my three step-children. Carl is the oldest. He did studies in visual arts at Edith Cowan University in WA. He is excellent at design, photography and editing. Carl and his partner Ryan, soon to be his wife, love to do disco work together. Carl has also travelled overseas a lot since completing university and he has been to some wild and out-of-the-way places. He is a very brave and interested traveler. He and Ryan lived for quite a while in Narooma and showed that they could get jobs in a very poor labour market. They worked in the wood fired pizza shop and followed the owners to help them set up a new restaurant in Berry. He and Ryan just completed twelve months travel in Canada, Thailand, Africa and India. Now they are establishing themselves in Melbourne. They are content to do any work while they work towards their ideal jobs.

David, who is the middle child, did an Arts Degree majoring in Aboriginal studies at Wollongong University. He has worked extensively in mentoring and preparing indigenous youth for employment and training. David has an interest in film-making and music. He and his wife Kate perform their own music together, as Hi-Life

Wedding, all around the world which is an amazing achievement. They made a fabulous music video in Taiwan with Carl doing the photography which they have used to promote themselves. They have also spent a lot of time teaching English in Taiwan which is where they held their wedding in October 2012. While this was a beautiful event it wasn't their official marriage. I wasn't well enough to go to Taiwan but we went to their official ceremony in David's mother's home. Clive's long-time friend Rob was the celebrant and David's grandmother and I had the honour of being one of the official witnesses. It was a nice feeling to be comfortable in the presence of Leonie's family and demonstrated that time tends to heal just about anything. Leonie was one of the first people to write to me after I was diagnosed with MND.

Lisa, who is the youngest, went to stay with friends in northern California for three months when she was just thirteen and went to school at the local school. She also came to China and coped very well in that environment. When she went to Wollongong University to study Exercise Science and Rehabilitation her overseas experience contributed to her gaining a scholarship to live in their international students residence. Lisa has also worked in London and in Canada and travelled in America and Europe during her twelve months overseas. She also volunteered to work with displaced children in Colombia. Lisa is an accomplished pianist and can also play the guitar, as do Carl and David. She has been working towards being a qualified yoga and Pilates teacher which she will complete in August 2013. Her partner Lachie is a Maths and Science teacher and they have recently moved from coastal Victoria to Melbourne and are in the process of settling in.

Clive and I consider Emma Morrison to be like a sixth child. We have known her since she was eighteen and now she is thirty-five, the same age as Carl. Emma got a degree in arts/law with first class-honours and then she did the extra study to be admitted to the bar. She has successfully worked in both private practice and the federal public service as a lawyer. Emma lives with her husband Greg in Canberra and she is the mother of Hannah (5), Max (3) and Ava (1). She is a wonderful mother and the three kids are all very smart. Clive and I have the good fortune of being a third set of grandparents to them. They call him Bear and me Chezza, and sometimes Chezza Bezza.

I know I will never see grandchildren of my own boys or from Clive's children so it has been a wonderful experience to have Emma's children in my life.

It has not been easy for Ashley having an old girlfriend so entrenched in his mother's life but she has been like a daughter to me ever since I met her. So I see Emma and now her family as a gift from Ashley, albeit an inadvertent one. I knew that it would be uncomfortable for him when I asked Emma and Greg and their two children Hannah and Max to come for New Year's Eve 2011, but he responded with good grace. Clive and I have spent a lot of New Years Eves with Emma. She also came to China to visit us, which adds to our bond.

I wanted as many of the people that I love to be there for New Year's Eve 2011. All the children came and it was everything I could have hoped for. I thought it was the start of my last year. I have been lucky that I got another year but I don't take anything for granted.

Clive and I are very proud of the achievements of our children and the blended family that we have built. They are all interesting people and we have such a good relationship with them all. Our friends enjoy their company and they have all been so caring to us over the past two years when we have needed their support and understanding. The great thing is they all genuinely enjoy catching up with each other whenever they can which indicates we must have done something right blending that family.

I know that they will all rally around Clive when the time comes for me to say goodbye.

CHAPTER 17

Leaving Darwin and Going to China

Clive was keen to live and work oversees but Customs only had three overseas postings so it had to be me who was going to have to try for it. I was fifty-two years old and hadn't applied for a job in about four years, so my confidence wasn't high. I dutifully wrote the application and submitted it and thought, that's it, they will knock me out in the short-listing process. When I heard that I had an interview I was in a panic. Most people don't like telephone interviews but I was glad that mine was. I was so nervous that I made myself a light brandy with lemonade and drank it during the interview so by the end I might have been a bit tipsy. I really thought that was it but apparently I did very well and became the first person from the Darwin office to win a placement overseas.

After the selection they send you a list of the available postings. So we filled that out having no idea about hardship posts and the allowances they attract. Some postings would not become vacant for as long as eighteen months. I always thought that was a poor way to do things — a lot can happen in twelve or eighteen months. While all of this was going on I had some varicose veins removed. I was on sick leave when Clive went to a management breakfast meeting where the guest speaker was the Consul

General from the Consulate in Guangzhou. He was so impressed with what she had to say about Guangzhou, that he phoned me and asked where had I put Guangzhou on the list? I said I don't think I mentioned it. So I phoned Canberra and got them to put Guangzhou as my first choice.

Guangzhou was a relatively new consulate and growing fast. The Immigration Section was even newer and they had been funded for a new position of Senior Immigration Officer, which they gave to me. The Chief Migration Officer phoned me to ask, how soon could I get to Guangzhou. They needed me as soon as possible. I explained that I had never had a posting before and really needed to do the overseas training course, which was in November, also fit in some language training and we needed to get packed and sort out arrangements with kids. We finally agreed on January 1999.

While I was in Canberra doing the training course I found out that the allowances we would get were considerable, which was a nice surprise. Guangzhou was considered a hardship post due to the pollution, the living conditions and the fact that there was only a very small expat community there so it would be hard to get a lot of the foods we were used to. Part of the allowance was so that you could afford the same things that you would get in Australia. You couldn't live that way anyway as the goods just weren't available. The only cheese we could find for ages was Bega cheese slices. We used to feed them to the dogs at home but we soon started using them to make cheese and Vegemite sandwiches.

Clive was a house-husband for a few weeks, so he

explored the wet market where locals bought meat, fish and vegetables, and the supermarkets. We also had to interview a maid, which was a unique situation for us. Mei Ling had never worked as a maid before and we had never had one so we thought we would make a good match. She was wonderful. She did the shopping for the meals she was going to cook for us each night. She couldn't speak English and our Mandarin was poor but we managed.

Lisa came with us for the first six months and was learning Mandarin at the American School so she was able to speak to Mei Ling before too long. She did well to manage because at home she was due to start Year Eleven but at the American School she had to do the last half of their Year Eleven and when she went back to Darwin do the last half again. It didn't do her any harm as she got into good study habits, decided on a career goal and got an excellent HSC score. I remember she was very disappointed at the initial interview when the principal said that they didn't have a chemistry teacher for Years 11 or 12. Lisa had already ascertained that she needed chemistry at Year 12 if she was to pursue studies in Exercise Physiology. A week later the principal rang and said they had obtained the services of a chemistry teacher and she would be taught one-on-one; she was thrilled.

Lisa settled into the foreign environment very well, except that one of our early meals was roast chicken. Mei Ling had cut it up and then arranged it on the plate as a whole chook complete with feet and head. Well, Lisa had a fit, so we had to tell Mei Ling no more heads and feet with our roast chicken.

We had a three-bedroom unit in the Garden Hotel, which was within walking distance of the office. It had the biggest foyer that I had ever seen. There was a security person by the lift and as we would get in they would press the button for our floor. We got so used to it that we would get in the lift at work and stand there before realising we had to press the button. There was a McDonalds in the bottom of our work building so that was a handy lunch option. After a while we weren't keen on having Chinese food for dinner and lunch.

Our unit was cleaned three times a week by the hotel staff and we got clean sheets each clean. They also gave us toilet paper and soap whether we needed it or not. It was too hard to turn off the tap and get it turned on when we needed toiletries so we took it all and used to give Mei Ling bags of the stuff for her family and friends. I started out doing our washing and washing the dishes at night until we realised Mei Ling didn't have enough to do. So we left the beds unmade, the dishes unwashed and she did the washing and ironing. If things needed mending she took them home and her husband did it. She used to take Clive's new trousers home to be taken up too. Other people would complain about their maids but we were perfectly happy with ours and we treated her well. She used to say we were too kind but we only treated her as we would anyone else.

The first three months for me at work were really stressful. They didn't have a proper desk for me. I had to use a table that was ergonomically too high for my computer and then the separate small computer desk was too low as it was built for Chinese people. So I was very uncomfortable, plus I was in charge of the Skilled Migration, Regional Migration and Temporary Business Visas and had no idea what I was doing. Because it was a relatively new office we had a pile of files that had been transferred from Beijing and they were in a precarious state.

It was already January and I had to make virtually the whole target for the skilled migration program for the office by the end of the financial year. I had a good team and we made the target with a lot of work. I used to go in on Saturdays with no overtime. It is hard in some countries to have the same standard of Occupational Health and Safety and ergonomics that we are used to at home. We had a refit of the office and worked on with dust and strong glue smells. In Australia we would have all walked out. There is some thought that heavy metals can trigger MND; well, there was every kind of pollutant in the air in Guangzhou, let alone the office.

I settled in and became competent. Early on I had one of those "six degrees of separation" incidents. One of the people I Interviewed for a Regional Migration sponsorship was for a chef for the Tarcutta RSL. When I read the file I couldn't believe it because my brother by this time was running a Post Office and mixed business in Tarcutta. I went to see him before heading off to China and he told me that the RSL Chinese restaurant had closed and moved to Tumut. I contacted the Sydney office and told them that they should check the validity of the employer nomination. They replied that it was OK. The applicant was a nice guy and sounded as if he could cook. The pieces of paper in China rarely had any validity, they were often forged. He had no idea of how small the place was that he was going to. End result, I granted the visa and I asked Brian when we came home if he ever went to Tumut and he said no, he went to Melbourne. So I figured he got a job somewhere in Melbourne and has probably made a good life for himself. He was either a friend or relative of the guy in Tarcutta.

I became quite good at assessing the bona fides of the chefs because of the training I had from Granny Fong. I would ask them how they would make sweet corn soup or fried rice and it was soon obvious if they could cook or not.

It was tough trying to prove the bonafides of the visa applicants for migration and even harder for visitor visas. You were always trying to judge whether they would return to China. It wasn't a good look if too many of your visa grants didn't come back. You would be looked at closely to see if you were committing fraud. Fortunately, our local Chinese staff were very good at checking documents etc, but then we had to keep an eye on them in case they were taking money to recommend someone for a visa.

Clive initially did some management training consultant work but it was easy to imagine how this could compromise a diplomat. After about nine weeks Clive got a job in the consulate working in the Family Migration Section. It was great because he was paid in US dollars and at the time the exchange rate was very good, so much so, that he was earning more than me but I brought the medical benefits, housing, maid and airfares for the kids. We lived well but not extravagantly and managed to save about $150,000 in the two years we were there. That really set us up.

Our weekends were always free so we could go out and look for furniture and "dong shi", which means things or "stuff". We had lots of places to explore and we would go out with Marcus and Kozie Loghem a lot of the time. It was their first overseas posting too, so we took them under our wing. Kozie was Japanese and could read characters and Marcus' Mandarin was better than mine and Clive had a good sense of direction so he generally knew where we were. He and I would use the buses for fun, only one Yuan (about 10 cents) each. We would get on and hope it was going where we wanted to go but we always knew we could get off and get a taxi. It was embarrassing at times because people would offer us their seats on the bus, even old ladies. Anyone who could speak a bit of English would try it out on us. The people of Guangzhou were great fun and tried to be as helpful as possible.

Marcus and Kozie had arrived in November 1999 so we were all there for Christmas. It was cold enough to wear a coat, but no snow as in the northern parts. On Christmas Eve when we left work to walk home there were lots of Chinese people wearing Christmas hats with lights on them and they were all saying Merry Christmas to us as we walked along. This occurred in a communist country that did not recognise Christianity. It was really lovely. The Garden Hotel had an enormous Christmas tree in the foyer and they were letting people in off the street to have their photo taken in front of it. For Christmas dinner all of the Australian consular staff went to the Sydney Restaurant for lunch, which was run by an Australian Chinese guy. The front of the bar was painted as a wave representing our surf culture.

After we had the consulate renovated, we had space for a social club and bar. The owner of the Sydney Restaurant used to import Four-and-Twenty pies for us to sell over the bar. I have never seen so much VB consumed in one place. There was a Dutch consular guy who could really put them away, both the pies and the beer. Clive was the president of the social club and it was making a lot of money because we got the grog duty-free. He thought that we should be supporting an orphanage or doing something in the community but the Foreign Affairs person who would have needed to arrange it wasn't interested. No doubt it would have been complicated.

Our first foray into buying furniture was on New Year's Day. We had a business card with the address and set off in a taxi along with Marcus and Kozie. We didn't know that the taxi drivers had no maps and if they went outside an area that they knew, they were as lost as us. After a while our taxi driver started pulling over and asking for directions. Clive phoned the factory and put the driver on the phone to get directions. Eventually we had two motorcycle outriders showing us the way. They took us off through market gardens and Marcus was sure that they were setting us up to be robbed. Finally we got there and sure enough the guy Tony was there with a warehouse full of furniture.

After we made our purchases and arrangements for delivery we set off home. First we had to wait for a taxi to come by but he could only take us so far so we hopped on a bus, which had Marcus in quite a state. The furniture was delivered OK, a coffee table and the altar table that is in the lounge. Eventually we sold the coffee table to Marcus and Kozie as I later found the day bed that is our lounge coffee table now. Clive had another one made from a slab of camphor wood. It was the one that I sold to a friend in China and then had to buy back because I could see that Clive was very disappointed. The friend was so nice he even said he would store it for us until we went home.

It was harder in Guangzhou than in Shanghai or Beijing because there was only a very small expatriate community whereas in the other cities there were thousands and so more people spoke English. Guangzhou was still a very Chinese city and we quite liked that. Every outing was an adventure. Grandpa Fong's village of Taishan was in Guangdong province and I had the information about it and even had a Chinese Migration Agent offer to go with me to interpret, as she knew the area. But it would have been too hard to explain my relationship with them without at least Ashley with me.

We had our first break after six months' back to Darwin. We thought Clive might need to have an operation on his shoulder which he had damaged while we were in Turkey, before we went to China. Apparently all of the swimming that he had been doing had freed it up. Our house in Leanyer was in a dreadful state so we spent a week cleaning it to give us some chance of selling it. The real estate agent who was a friend of ours had been useless. Eventually we sold it but it was Clive who did all of the negotiating and we still had to pay the agent. It was on that trip that we bought the house in Canberra, which hadn't been on our agenda. We had just been checking out the market and fell over something we really liked. We celebrated by having a night in Narooma and I fell in love with the beauty of it and the clear blue water.

Clive did have a health scare when we were returning through Darwin about the time of the invasion of East Timor. He had dreadful stomach pains and was admitted to Darwin hospital but they were so busy with Timor casualties that they released him to fly back to China. We arrived in Guangzhou and he became very ill and was evacuated to Hong Kong in a mini-bus they called an ambulance. It was a scary time for me as we drove the four hours to Hong Kong as his condition got worse. Fortunately the care in the hospital in Hong Kong was amazing and his gall-bladder, which had adhered to the liver, was removed in a lengthy operation.

We walked out with a bill for over $35,000 dollars and knew we would have to make a contribution based on the costs that would have been incurred in Australia. Clive was very nervous when he got the bill but our contribution was only $125.

The whole world was generally in panic over the year 2000 and all of the things that were predicted to go wrong because of computers. Naturally it was thought that China would be a basket case so we volunteered to stay and not take holidays at that time and let the people with families go. Well, not a thing went wrong. That was also the year of the Sydney Olympics and Clive's fiftieth birthday. As usual, Clive was well organised and had tickets for some of the events. We went to Melbourne where he celebrated his birthday with family and friends, then we went on to

Sydney to the games. All of Clive's children came too, Ashley was already living in Sydney. Our friends from California, Mark and Joan, were also there. So it was quite a time of reunion with family and friends.

To continue on about China, after a year Clive arranged for us to move out of the hotel to a unit in a complex on Ersha Island in the middle of the Pearl River. There we had a small balcony, a better gym and pool and it was easier to meet expats who weren't from the consulate. We used to walk out of our door and across the courtyard to the gym or pool, then have a shower and go into the breakfast room and eat, then back to our unit to get dressed and out to the gate where our taxi driver would be waiting to take us the 6 km to work. When we first moved we had to go out to the road and hail a taxi, which didn't give us much control over when we would get to work. So one morning we found a guy we liked and got one of the young expats who could speak Mandarin to negotiate for us and he was there every morning. We got ourselves home at night because we didn't leave at a regular time. When Carl stayed on in Guangzhou after we left and got a job in the consulate he ended up using our same taxi driver.

It was always a concern if you became ill or had to go to the dentist, as I did. I got a terrible pain and knew I was in trouble and we hunted down a dentist who had some training in Germany. After a long trip we located a building called the Department of Stomatology which is "English" for teeth. The dentist was a lovely man who explained I needed root canal treatment and then gave me the news that novacaine was in very short supply. He then explained that "pain-free dentistry" was a western concept. To which I replied it was concept I really liked. He did a great job to fix me up temporarily and when I returned to complete the job he had managed to import some novacain from Hong Kong. It was pretty obvious I was getting special treatment as all patients were lined up in stalls, much like a shearing shed, and you could see and hear everything. I must say I felt a little guilty about that as all the other patients had to go without. Straight after the dentist we boarded an overnight train for Yangshou and Guilin for a short break and it was a tough trip.

We had a fantastic trip to Harbin in northern China during the last winter we were there. Harbin was occupied by Russia for many years and is a fascinating place. Clives three kids came with us and it was a unique experience to get off the plane into -30 Degrees Celsius. I still remember Lisa exclaiming "Dad, the boogers in my nose are frozen". David was convinced he was getting frostbite and we kept telling him if he could still feel his feet he was OK. Harbin has an Ice Festival every year and there were magnificent ice carvings throughout the town. We spent the three days there rugged up and were astounded watching the locals walk around in relatively light clothing. It was a memorable trip for us all.

That same winter Clives mate Rob (Arra) and his wife Wendy visited us and we travelled to Beijing by train. Always it amazed us just how many people were on the move in China and how well the transport system coped. I have great memories of flying across a frozen lake in the Beijing Winter Gardens, being pushed in a sled by a very fit young Chinese entrepreneur.

I could go on and on with China stories but I think you get the idea of what it was like. We enjoyed and respected the people enormously. We butchered their language and I don't know how many other things we may have done wrong but we were treated kindly, given respect just because we were foreigners, often seen as a curiosity and we had lots of laughs with them. I remember Clive taking his shirt off in a market to try on a shirt and people freaking out yelling in Cantonese. I suspect the translation was "hairy monster". Overall we enjoyed our time there immensely.

The woman replacing me was single but I convinced her to keep Mei Ling who had been good enough to move with us even though it meant further travel for her. When we were at the hotel she would wait until we came home but we said she should not do that when we moved, that we were quite OK to heat our meal in the microwave. This meant that we didn't see her so much but sometimes she would stay when we had guests and we would give her the money for a taxi. When we had anyone around who spoke Cantonese or Mandarin I could tell her how much we thought of her. I knew that I wasn't going to be able to keep in touch with her but I did send her a card via one of our Australian Chinese friends so she would know that we had not forgotten her.

We extended our posting by three months and in retrospect probably should have extended for a full year or tried to cross-post. At the time we were concerned as Clive had been out of Customs for over two years and it was going to be difficult to re-establish his career.

CHAPTER 18

Leaving China and Settling in Canberra

We already had the new house in Canberra, and we were looking forward to moving in and placing the Chinese furniture which we had selected specifically for the house. That was all good but we didn't reckon on the reverse culture shock that returning from a posting would create. In part it was because we didn't go back to Darwin but also we were unprepared for the type of work in Central Office.

We both had trouble adjusting to working in Canberra. The promotion that I had applied for while still in China came through so I moved into an area that I was unfamiliar with and as it turned out it was a big mistake. I had trouble with the winter, driving in the dark and the woman who was my boss. I knew that I had signs of depression and saw a lovely doctor and tried to push through it. I had some leave and all I wanted to do was stay in bed or inside. That was when I knew that I was in trouble and went onto anti-depressant medication. Clive wasn't faring much better in the work environment either.

At this time there was the infamous Tampa affair when the Prime Minister John Howard refused to let a Norwegian vessel unload rescued refugees at Christmas Island. Clive and I were appalled at the shameful decision to change the refugee policy on the run. This incident definitely contributed to our cynicism about the public service and the policy we were being asked to implement, and no doubt hastened our retirements.

We missed the more meaningful work that we had done overseas and in Darwin. In that work we were used to making decisions and meeting objectives. Nothing that we did in Canberra seemed relevant. I for one was too old and unwilling to make the necessary adjustments to my skill set in order to work successfully in Central Office.

Canberra for me has always been a place where I felt that I didn't fit. While we were enjoying the house and keeping up with our friends in Canberra, Clive was worried about me and we felt that we had made a mistake and should have done another year in China and then tried to cross-post.

CHAPTER 19

Moving to Live in Narooma

Our first holiday, we came to Narooma and in our usual impulsive way we bought the block at 21 Gem Crescent. Then we began trying to work out how we could get to live here as soon as possible as I had decided that as soon as I turned fifty-five that I would get out of the public service. We used to come to Narooma regularly to work out whether to build or buy and we stayed at Cooinda Holiday Apartments, which is how we met our good friends Jan and Bruce Rapkins.

Clive even applied for a job with Centrelink in Narooma and considered real estate work. On one of our visits he said to Bruce, "let us know if you ever decide to sell". That was in late 2001 and in the New Year Bruce said that they were thinking of selling so we agreed the price and the two blokes shook hands and we had a deal. Jan and Bruce said that they thought around September would suit them and we didn't pay them until about June after they found a house they wanted to buy.

We sold up in the August and took over Cooinda. Lots of people thought we were crazy doing the deal that way but it proved right. Prices had started to rise and Clive asked Bruce if he wanted to increase his price as there was no contract. Bruce said no as they had been able to buy their new house at a good price. This demonstrated to us what a man of integrity Bruce was. His word was his bond. People also said, why didn't we bargain, but Clive knew that the price was fair and later as we got to know Bruce we knew that it had been the right way to approach things. He had a fair price on it and if we had tried to lower the price we wouldn't have got the place. In the end it proved to be a bonanza for us and we have never regretted a moment of our life here.

Even though we only ran the units for eighteen months we had a business plan for three years, which we had achieved in the eighteen months. We built the business from a $40,000 per annum business to $80,000. The conditions for local tourism were very favourable during that time as there had been 9/11, the Bali bombing and SARS, so people weren't travelling overseas so much. We introduced holiday packages and increased our rates but still gave the same rates to our old clients, who used to come and stay for two or three weeks. We were in a good location to take overnighters who often turned into regulars. When we filled up we would send overnighters to Margaret and Bill Falls at Inlet Views Motel which was located just behind us. That was the start of another lasting friendship.

We were in good shape to sell when we did. Clive had recently had an evaluation done and as we didn't plan to sell at the time we asked for the top price, never dreaming that we would get it. Our books were all certified by an accountant too so we could prove our takings and occupancy rates. Little did we know that the market would soon change, and it would never again be as buoyant as it had been while we were running Cooinda. People started holidaying overseas once again and the oldies got too old to drive to Narooma or had died and working people were taking shorter holiday breaks. We were very lucky with our little foray into small business.

As well as having a great time running the business we made a good living and achieved a capital gain of over $300,000 in the eighteen months we owned it. For people like us you usually have to work a very long time to make that amount of money. This justified all of the risks about leaving the Public Service and set us up financially in a way we could not have dreamed of.

This experience in small business did demonstrate to both of us that the skills and work ethic we had learned in twenty plus years in the Public Service were valuable and transferable.

CHAPTER 20

Indigenous Mentor Course

W e sold Cooinda much sooner than planned and were not quite ready for retirement. At about the same time, our friend Paul Nixon was developing a fairly busy business consulting in Indigenous Employment and Training. Paul had a falling out with his partners and decided to go his own way. He asked Clive to help him develop a certified course in Indigenous Mentoring for his company Employment and Training Outcomes (ETO).

Clive and Paul were natural trainers and had worked together going back to 1983. The three of us headed up to Darwin and moved into the beach front apartment we owned in Nightcliff. Paul and Clive wrote the course and developed all the training materials and then piloted the course with 25 participants from the Northern Territory.

The course was a great success and we thought we might deliver four or five courses around the country. However it turned out to be very well received and over the next four years we delivered the Indigenous Mentoring Course to over 700 participants (mostly indigenous trainees) in every state in Australia.

I was happy to help out with the administration of the course as there was a lot of organising to do with a week of residential training. However, over time I began helping with trainees who had literacy issues and eventually increased my role in the training delivery. Clive and Paul encouraged me to do this and had a lot more confidence in my ability than I did. As a result I obtained my Certificate IV in Training and Assessment and became a fully qualified trainer.

The three of us had some great times travelling around the country and some of the indigenous people we worked with were inspirational in their efforts to help their people. It was demanding but very rewarding work and a very successful course financially for Paul's company. Clive and I even established our own consulting firm, Quickmatch Consulting, to take on work that Paul was unable to do himself.

I had worked closely with Aboriginal people as far back as 1964 when I started nursing and had great affection and respect for traditional Aboriginal people and their culture. Paul who is Irish has an incredible understanding of Indigenous culture and ran a brilliant Cultural Awareness program. Clive had also worked with Aboriginal people in the CES and in Customs. It was this knowledge and respect by the trainers that was the key to the success of the Indigenous Mentoring Course. The promotional video we developed for the course can still be viewed on the ETO website or on YouTube: Search for "ETO Indigenous Mentor Course Participant Responses". You even get to see me talking before I was silenced by MND.

At one stage we did a big road trip travelling around Australia to deliver the course in the NT and Western Australia. We left Narooma and travelled to Alice Springs, Darwin, Kununurra, Broome, Geraldton and Perth, delivering the course along the way. We could not rely on accommodation in Northern Australia in the dry Season so we had to take a trailer and tent with us to use in the more remote places.

While we were in Darwin staying with my son Paul, we left the trailer at the Fong family home where my ex-husband David was living. Clive and I decided we had better give the tent a trial run so we went to David's place to do this. It turned out it wasn't as easy to work out as Paul had told us, so David kindly offered to help us set it up. In any case I ended up inside the tent holding the poles while Clive and David erected the tent on the outside. I remember having this odd thought, "Here I am putting up a tent with my two husbands"!

We camped for the first time in Kununurra and were reasonably happy that we had got set up even if we did need a hand from the much more experienced grey nomads camped all around us. I asked Clive to get a globe for the reading light and as he drove off I realised the Engel fridge was still plugged into the socket in the back of the Pajero. We made quite a hit in the campground as Clive drove off obliviously towing the fridge with me chasing behind, trying to stop him before he got on the highway. I think that was the last of our camping adventures.

Through Quickmatch Clive and I did get involved with an interesting project with a friend of ours, Jamie Bell-Towers, who lived in the unit behind our house in Gareth Avenue.

Jamie was working with a consortium trying to get approval to build a seniors living estate in Moruya, NSW. It was a very exciting concept based on the ideas of Dr Hans Becker who was a world leader in seniors living from the Netherlands. Our role would have been to train and place indigenous people to work in the construction phase and then place people to work on a full-time basis in the facility.

The plans allowed for people to live in a wide range of situations, from totally independent dwellings to medium, and high-care living even to the point of having a dementia care facility. The complex had plans for a range of excellent amenities including a pool, boutique theatre, library and IT centre as well as a village mall where people could buy a paper, have a coffee, etc.

Clive and I even travelled to visit one of Hans Becker's seniors living facilities in Rotterdam and were very impressed with how the whole system worked. The philosophy of the business was that old people should not be isolated from the community and every effort was made to stimulate people to stay active. I thought about some of the depressing aged care centres we have in this country and how much better we could do with a more innovative approach to the design of such facilities.

Unfortunately the project was hampered the whole way by a very staid bureaucratic approach from the local council and after three years of battling with the town planning people the project fell over. Moruya missed the opportunity to establish a facility with world's best practice in seniors living.

As it turns out, I need not worry about living in a depressing aged care situation but I think about the hundreds of people on the South Coast who could have had so much better.

One good outcome that occurred as part of the time working with indigenous people was that we became friends with the owner of a steel fabrication business in Moruya, Mordek. Unlike a lot of employers he was prepared to give indigenous people a go and took on a number of recruits. One guy we placed there, Brett, had been through a tough time and I became his mentor. It was very satisfying to see him succeed and change his life for the better.

CHAPTER 21

Special Places

Together Clive and I have done a lot of travel and been to some lovely places. My favourite places in the world are New York for its buzz, Bora Bora for its unique experience and Ningaloo Reef in Western Australia and Lady Elliot Island for their wonderful snorkelling experiences. I am forever grateful that somehow I must have mentioned in Ashley's presence that I would love to go to Bora Bora and it stuck in his mind. He gave Clive and me a trip there as a birthday present from him and Paul and insisted that we stay in the over-water bungalows. I burst into tears when I saw the viewing window in the floor.

Clive and I decided after I was diagnosed that we would do whatever trips we could, especially those involving snorkelling. Our second trip to Bora Bora was equally marvellous though the weather wasn't quite as good. We went with Doug and Lydia and stayed at the same place. The staff remembered us so we got even more excellent treatment. If you want a definition of paradise, Bora Bora comes very close.

I fell in love with Ningaloo Reef the first time we went there, which was around my sixtieth birthday. It was too late in the season for the whale sharks, but the reef there can be accessed directly from the beach. The fish life and turtles and reef sharks are amazing. On our next trip we had the awe-inspiring chance to swim with seven whale sharks as well as manta rays. We did a third trip there after we knew that I had MND. This time we flew to Perth with Jan and Bruce and borrowed our friend Nico's caravan, which was fairly new and ideally set up for two couples. It was my first stay in a caravan since cyclone Tracy. We had a great trip with very dear friends.

I have mentioned our trip to the Whitsundays but in May 2013 we went to Lady Elliot Island which is another special place — a small coral cay located at the most southern tip of the Barrier Reef. This is an expensive trip because the island is 80 km off the coast from Bundaberg and the only access is by plane. We stayed in a two-bedroom unit with the lagoon only twenty metres from our door. I got to swim with lots of turtles and some were so tame that you could tickle them under their flippers. We had windy rainy weather but the water was warm with a wet suit on and the last day it was fine and I had the best snorkel, which I think may be my last.

My favourite snorkel spots here in Narooma are Glass House Rocks, the third hole of the Golf Club, Dalmeny and the Board Walk. I want my ashes spread in one of them and I think Clive will choose Glass House Rocks. It would be good if my boys could do it with him, even better if Carl, David, Lisa, Kate, Ryan, Lachie, Emma and Greg could do a group snorkel on a lovely sunny autumn day. Maybe get some fish and abalone and go back home and have a party with lots of music, and all of you cooking together. That would be a good send off.

CHAPTER 22

Family and Friends

I have never been much for joining community organisations — except for the Labor Party in Darwin — and neither has Clive. In Narooma we met people through running Cooinda, like Marg and Bill from Inlet Views Motel and Luisa and Max from Sorrisos Italian Restaruant who have become dear friends. We bought the house in Gareth Avenue at the time we sold Cooinda as we weren't sure whether we wanted to take on the task of building. We were clearing the block one day and met the new owner of 19 Gem Crescent, who was Doug Woodhouse. Once we got to know him and his wife Lydia Morton we decided that we would go ahead and build. We spent ages coming up with a design that would work on the block and meet all of Council's restrictions.

We are now into our sixth year living in the house and we still love it. With all "Grand Designs" you can think you should have done this or that and we have had those thoughts, but not enough to make us dissatisfied with what we have. There are always the things that you wished that you had spent more money on but as you get to the end, when you are doing the finishing, that is when you realise that you are running out of money. The best thing is that all of our kids love coming here and we have had some great times with family and friends. Christmas 2011 when we had everyone home is a wonderful memory for me and I think it had a consolidating effect on our family. It is a beautiful house in a gorgeous location and I only wish I could stay here to the end.

Clive says that friendship is often a matter of geography and that has proved to be the case for us. Doug and Lydia are more like family. They were both very successful in their careers with Foreign Affairs. When Lydia became the Ambassador in The Hague, Netherlands, we visited them and stayed in the magnificent residence.

Lydia is a very competent women. She is an international lawyer and speaks Chinese and French fluently but, more importantly she is my mate who has a tendency for the occasional "whoopsie', not unlike my dear husband. Lydia, I know, has committed herself to supporting me through MND. She could have taken up any of a number of lucrative and challenging work offers when she returned from her role as the Australian Ambassador in The Hague. She has chosen instead to be a most dear and supportive friend and I know she will pay a heavy price for her determined support.

Doug is a little more like me in terms of the domestic management but has proved to be a wonderful friend. Doug had the experience of caring for his first wife who died of cancer. He has an innate understanding of what I am going through with a terminal illness and he gives me enormous peace of mind as I head towards the end of my time.

Nothing is too much trouble for them and we spend a lot of time together. They open their homes in Canberra and Narooma to us and our family members and friends.

We have already had three holidays with them, to Bora Bora, the Whitsundays yacht trip and to Lady Elliot Island. They also came to Darwin in July 2013 where we took great delight in showing them around. My son Paul was keen to have them stay with us in his newly refurbished unit. Both Clive and I have come to rely on their friendship and the amount of time that they spend here in Narooma with us. We laugh a lot and share meals (not me now) and it boosts our spirits to have them in our life.

Margaret and Allan Osborne up the road have also become close friends and they again can't do enough for us. Alan and Doug together with Clive have formed a mini "Men's Club", centred around doing up Clive's boat, initially. Now they do a multitude of jobs together where Clive comes in for a shellacking over just about everything. His tools aren't in good repair, he is too gung-ho, clumsy etc. To listen to them you would think that they were enemies, not the best mates that they really are. Margaret, Lydia and I are much more polite in how we conduct our friendship!

Jan and Bruce Rapkins bring us in wood from their farm and remain firm friends. Marg and Bill Falls, although pretty caught up in running their businesses, would be here instantly if we need them. Since I can't enjoy a lunch or have much stamina for the shopping days we used to have together, Jan and Marg come to the movies with me.

More recent friends Ruth and Bernie Perret and Jan and Rob Atkinson come to visit often. Our friends in Canberra and Victoria keep in contact, to see how we are going, to the extent that Clive feels like a broken record at times having to give an update on me.

Tom and Heather Calma live in Canberra and visit us when they can. Tom is very highly recognised for his work on behalf of Indigenous people. He was awarded an AO and nominated for Australian of the year as well as receiving honorary doctorates. However to me Dr Tom Calma is just Tom the friend I have known for forty-five years who loves to come to Narooma and eat anything from the ocean. Heather, Tom's wife, has been a supportive friend to both Clive and I since we got together back in Darwin in the eighties and is a delightful woman to spend time with.

A great friend from Narooma and Canberra is Andy Finlay and his lovely wife, Mary. Andy was a mate of Clive's going back to football days in Warrnambool in the seventies. He was a popular and enthusiastic MC at Clive's sixtieth birthday party.

Andy is a unique character who is probably the most effusive and supportive person I have ever met. People who don't know him often misjudge him. They often think he is over the top but Andy is the most genuine person, particularly in his admiration of people he respects. I often say if you are feeling a little flat and you get a call from Andy you are soon up again. Andy's life is dedicated to extolling the achievements and virtues of his friends. When Clive speared three fish in one shot at Montague Island Andy told everyone in Narooma about this "legendary" achievement, even badgering the editor of the Narooma news to include an article about the event.

Since I was diagnosed with MND Andy has rung every Friday night for two and half years. He always wants to help and is very generous always buying me flowers. He has a lovely unit in Narooma that is all on one level and he offered it to us to live in if I got to a stage where I could not get up the stairs in our house.

There is also another Andy, Andy Foster, who lives nearby when he is not working as a skipper on a ship in the petroleum industry. I met Andy through a friend in Narooma and in one of those odd coincidences worked out that he had been in the same class as my son Paul in Darwin. Obviously he is the same age as my son but he is always keen to see me when in Narooma on leave.

Andy offered to take me on a sailing trip to the Whitsundays. I think he knew how well this would work for me, given my love of the ocean and the difficulty I had with travelling. He skippered the magnificent 53-foot yacht and our very close friends came for ten days. I was able to snorkel and enjoy the companionship but could rest up any time of day in our luxurious cabin. Andy gave us a wonderful time, which he was able to do because of his intimate knowledge of the Barrier Reef waters and his skills as a sailor. I was deeply touched that he would dedicate himself so selflessly to showing me such a wonderful time.

Iolanda and Juergen our friends who live in Sydney in an apartment with a view of the bridge and the Opera House, open their home to us and often even, our kids. Whenever we go to Sydney for visits to my neurologist or need to stop over prior to a flight somewhere we stay with them. We had a holiday with them to Norfolk Island where we hoped to do snorkeling but the weather was poor; however there was so much history and some good-duty free shopping that we had a great time anyway.

Iolanda and Juergen, were living in Hong Kong when we were in China which was where our joint friendship started. Clive and Iolanda had joined the CES in Melbourne at the same time so they were old friends. They were living in Sydney during the Olympics in 2000 so we stayed with them and shared that experience. Then they moved to Malaysia for about five years and again we used to visit and had some joint trips together there. Our family has a long history of experiencing Iolanda and Juergen's marvellous hospitality and friendship.

Clive has a great family: garrulous, loving and fun. We have had constant loving support from Clive's sister Margaret and her husband Murray. Margaret has sent me so many lovely gifts including two fluffy throws which I love and use a lot. Unfortunately Buster really likes them too and sneaks onto them when I am not looking. They are still running a farm and can't often get away but they have visited us here and we are always made welcome at the farm which is a quiet getaway place. As well as running the farm Murray works as an orderly at the Geelong Hospital. It was Murray who came up with some great solutions to my MND-related problems. It has been a great privilege to have them as my in-laws.

Clive's younger brother Craig, who is an Anglican Minister, his wife Merle and their two children Meredith and Jonathon keep me in their prayers for which I thank them.

Then there is Clive's cousin Doug and his wife Carol. Doug is a little older than Clive but they are more like brothers than cousins since they grew up only a few houses away from each other. Their mothers who were sisters were inseparable. They have so many funny stories of their time growing up. Doug is reputed to have bitten a small baby in a pram when he was about three and when asked why he did it, he said, "Because he was giving me cheek!" He once staked Clive out in the backyard American Indian style and poured honey on him so the ants would eat him. It's amazing they are still such good mates. Carol has become a wonderful friend and is part of some great travel memories in France and the Netherlands and on our Whitsundays sailing trip. She is a fervent skinny dipper as am I but when she starts laughing climbing down a ladder into the water, watch out below! They too open their home to us whenever we go to Melbourne. You can't be down in the dumps for too long around those two. They are such fun.

All of our children and partners have shared a lot of time with us in this house, especially in the last two years. They all try to visit as much as they can and to help out. Emma and Greg bring Hannah, Max and Ava to see us and what a delight it is to have fun with the kids.

My brother Brian and I have never been close for no particular reason, that is; we have never had a serious disagreement that caused the distance. When I rang him to tell him I had MND he decided he had better tell me he had been diagnosed with lung cancer.

I think it's fair to say that I have done most of the work on our relationship. At the time of his divorce I gave him all of the support that I could because he had no one and I knew that his wife had her family. Even when he came to live in Narooma and we offered him work at Cooinda he really kept me at arm's length. I don't think he liked that he was working for us whereas we wanted him to take an interest and take over some aspects of running the place. We weren't looking for an employee, rather a collaborator. He was in a pretty vulnerable place ego-wise, having lost so much as everybody does in a divorce. You are faced with starting over and are financially less well off. So working with his older sister in her business was obviously hard to take after having owned and lost his small business.

Brian has been a bit of a rolling stone but he has managed to find work in Wagga and then in Darwin. Now that we are both sick (he with cancer of the lung) we are as close as we are ever going to be. He is still prickly at times and, gender aside, we couldn't be more different, except we have the same work ethic that we got from Mum. It is a Treuel characteristic.

Brian lived in Darwin from age nine to his mid-twenties and has a strong attachment to Darwin as a place of good memories and friends. I think that is why he returned there a few years ago. When his illness began, he was in a supportive work environment and had good friends around him plus the distraction of his beloved Waratahs Football Club. He has moved from Darwin back to Wagga Wagga in the hopes of improved treatment and to be close to his daughters Kelly and Sarah and to his granddaughter Sienna. Philip his son remains in Darwin for the time being.

I couldn't discuss my friends without mentioning my mate, Matt. Matt inherited MND from his father, like I did, when he was in his thirties. The odds of having two familial MND sufferers in a town the size of Narooma are not worth contemplating. However, here we are. We don't catch up that often and there are probably good reasons for that, but when we do there is a special bond that would be hard for others to understand. Matt has a lovely wife Steph who visits as a community nurse (small town, Narooma).

They have three young children, so the fact that Matt has survived ten years with reasonable quality of life is a joy for me. Keep hanging in there, Matt my friend.

CHAPTER 23

Living with MND

For me MND has been both a curse and a blessing. The curse bit is that it will cut my life shorter than I expected. I really thought that I would get into my seventies at least. The irony of it is that both Brian and I will have our lives shortened by about ten years compared with our parents. I am mortified that I may have passed the defective gene that causes familial MND on to one or both of my boys and we can't yet find out which gene it is.

When we had Clive's sixtieth birthday party in early October 2010 I made a speech and it was shortly after that that I noticed some slurring of my speech. When I mentioned it to others they said they couldn't notice it. I let it go until by March 2011. I knew that it was getting worse and so I got referred to a neurologist in Canberra. He did blood tests to eliminate a number of things including stroke and Myasthenia Gravis. MND was in the back of my mind so I was hoping that it was Myasthenia Gravis, which could not be cured but there was treatment which allowed you to live for a long time, compared with MND.

I remember April Fools Day 2011 was the day in Canberra that my concerns were more or less confirmed, and in a pretty brutal way, by a thoughtless specialist. Ash had been home for a visit and he was flying back to

London that day. I called him at the airport to tell him, and I remember asking him to stay close to Paul. That shows what a state Clive and I were in, standing in the car-park of the Medical Centre. I was behaving as if I was going to die there and then. At most I thought I would have a year, going by what had happened to Dad.

Clive rang the contact number of a neurologist in Sydney and the earliest appointment we could get was 10 June . The specialist in Canberra didn't even spend enough time telling us in detail about the choices we had. When Clive said, "What if we have to wait weeks to get an appointment'" he just said, "Well if it is familial MND, then it doesn't really matter about a delay". The fact is, it does matter because the sooner you go onto Rilutek, the better.

We didn't know what to do with ourselves. We were supposed to stay with our friends Heather and Tom Calma for the weekend and I said to Clive that we couldn't possibly take this situation to them. Clive asked, did I want to go to a hotel or go home, and I said in desperation, just drive around. Then Heather phoned us to see how we had got on and she insisted that we go there. When we got there she had a bottle of champagne open and we proceeded to get tipsy. Tom came home and we all laughed and cried together. They really looked after us.

Fortunately for us, whilst we for once didn't have our usual bias for action, our dear girl Emma did. April 1 was a Friday and by Monday afternoon she had tracked down Professor Dominic Rowe, at Macquarie Neurology in Sydney and they had said we could have an appointment on Tuesday afternoon if we wanted it. Apparently Dominic always kept a few vacant spots so he could respond to people caught like us.

From day one when Dominic came out to the waiting room to meet us, I had a good feeling. He said, "Hello, I am Dominic. Please come in" He is so personable, we either call him Dom or Prof. He has the ability to deal with a dying person and somehow get them to see that they are now living with MND and not just dying of it. He outlines all of the allied health professionals that he has attending his regular MND clinics and what they can do to help you. I have never seen Dom when he hasn't made me feel better just because he cares. He gives me a kiss and a hug and the world feels OK for a while. While admitting that there was no cure and only one drug (Rilutek) available, the impact of which was hard to measure, he did say that a wholistic management plan could give quality of life.

On day one I raised end-of-life issues with him. The most confronting thing I was dealing with on my first visit to Dominic was the prospect of a difficult, painful and undignified journey leading to an inevitable ghastly death. To an extent I had seen this with my father. Dominic outlined how much progress had been made in managing MND progression in the twenty or so years since my father's death. He assured me this would never be the case for me and with quality clinical care I would have control of my destiny by being able to make decisions on what medical interventions I would agree to.

As a result I wrote a living will outlining my medical wishes. I cannot explain what a comfort it was to have this support and after that I never feared MND again. He put my mind at rest about that and said, "I am in this with you the whole way." Even just to see him and receive his hug and kiss does wonders. I felt like I was in the best hands possible. Clive once asked him about the emotional cost that goes with getting close to so many people who die. Let's face it, there are plenty of medical professionals who remain aloof. Dom said simply, "If you can't give of yourself, then you are in the wrong profession."

All of the office staff at Macquarie Neurology are very responsive and know every patient by name. You are made to feel part of a special family. Dominic has set up a multi-disciplinary clinic where the patient stays in one room and all of the allied health professionals come to you. He has a pulmonary doctor, dietician, speech pathologist, physiotherapist, social worker, occupational therapist and a representative from MND NSW. I attend about every three months and reports are sent to my GP and my local dietician and speech pathologist.

Dominic is determined to find a cure for MND and to that end he has obtained funding and gathered a team of researchers and scientists into a purpose built research facility at Macquarie University. They are working in a collaborative way to find the root cause of MND and from there to find treatment and cure. It is a massive task but I have toured the research facility and met some of the people working there and they are an impressive lot and dedicated to the task. It helps me to know that Dominic is so passionate about finding a cure for MND that I believe his team of researchers will do it. As yet I don't know what gene mutation I have that has caused my familial MND but Dom has met my two sons and I know that he continues to work on my behalf. I made a donation recently to the Macquarie Research Foundation and have told my friends to donate if they wish rather than sending flowers to my funeral.

By the end of the first week I had had muscle tests that confirmed familial MND. I was put on Rilutek immediately, the only drug available that seems to slow the progress of the disease down by about three months. We also started the gene testing process.

So began the process of living with MND and naturally you start researching and coming to terms with your new life. I was aware that MND is not predictable in its progression and that the average survival time was two to three years.

I believe Doctors voted MND as the disease they would least like to contract. I am not sure why but I suspect it's because it chips away at your capacity as the motor neurones start failing in their job of stimulating muscle movement. Essentially this means a steady deterioration into paralysis while your mental capacity remains intact.

The natural response of someone diagnosed with a terminal illness is to fight the disease. You so often hear terms like 'his battle with cancer' and 'she fought it to the end'. With some illnesses a positive mindset and a preparedness to endure radical treatment may win the day. MND is not like this, and I concluded early in the journey that I needed to live with the disease rather than "fight" some battle I was destined to lose. The reality is that MND always runs its course and you don't survive but it doesn't mean that you have to give up on life. In fact in some ways the MND diagnosis provides opportunities to enhance the life you have in ways you could not have dreamed.

Clive and I quickly discovered that the other drug that, anecdotally, seems to help is cannabis but because it is illegal in Australia there have never been any serious clinical trials. I use both drugs because the Rilutek is proven and the cannabis seems to help with the symptoms. Cannabis is legally prescribed in a number of states in the USA as a drug for MND or ALS (as it is known there).

When you have so few options it's worth experimenting even if the concept of smoking marijuana was a totally alien to me. However having a bunch of children with broad life experience can be useful and I was very quickly able to get my hands on some cannabis. I could not face the prospect of smoking as I have never been able to smoke so Clive found a vaporiser on the net and I was a fully-fledged druggie in no time. Ironically I never really got "high" on the drug as it seemed to target the symptoms I had and I did get significant relief.

It was particularly useful when I got soreness in the diaphragm and it relieved and relaxed me at bedtime. All in all it was a positive and amusing diversion for me at a traumatic time just after diagnosis and provided great amusement to all the kids who pointed out that they had matured and were over the cannabis scene. I also had a brief career as a drug pusher when friends would call for coffee and be rewarded with a hash brownie that I enjoyed when I could still eat. I did use cannabis daily and that presented some difficulties when I travelled because it is an illegal drug. I used to carry a clinical trial report from the USA which proclaimed the benefits of the drug. I figured I would show this to any arresting officer if I was caught and if they wanted to charge me, then so be it.

As I mentioned in the introduction I made a decision with Dominic's great encouragement to see MND as something I was living with rather than trying to fight it. I had decided to use my energy to live my life now rather than trying to maintain a life that was now gone.

Once I made this decision my life became focused on getting everything I could out of the time I had left. I don't mean just the bucket list, although Clive ensured we had some fantastic trips and experiences. Probably more importantly I made a conscious effort to tell those close to me what I really thought and felt. I have been able to communicate more honestly and directly with people in the last two years than I did in the previous twenty. Not only was I able to express myself more easily, I found people, especially my children, were so open to a level of intimacy that I doubt was possible without my illness. It should never be underestimated how valuable that sort of communication is but it is also why it's so difficult. I will leave this world knowing that I did not leave important messages undelivered.

As I have mentioned the first symptoms for me were the slurred speech related to the loss of function in my tongue and throat. A result of this was a constant flow of saliva and drool that made public exposure very difficult and embarrassing for me. Dominic and I tried a range of treatments. I took a drug called Endep to try and slow the flow down. I had Botox injections which were costly (they were not covered by private or public health insurance) and had a marginal impact. I became so frustrated with the problem that Dominic referred me to a radiologist who radiated my saliva glands in the hope of reducing the uncontrollable flow.

Nothing seemed to work until a visit from Clive's sister Margaret and her husband Murray. Murray is a farmer who also works as an orderly at Geelong Hospital in Victoria. He observed me struggling with this drooling for a few days and suggested I use surgical masks with tissues on the inside. It was such a simple and practical solution and it gave me enormous freedom to be in public view again. Although I did have one clown in the supermarket ask me if I was going to rob the store because I was masked.

Murray also came up with a simple fix that allowed me to feed through the Percutaneous Endoscopic Gastrostomy (PEG) whilst driving long distances. We had been discussing how it was such a difficulty trying to fit in ten hours of feeding per day. As we got in the car to leave their farm Murray ran to the barn and came back with a piece of tubing and a bit of twine. In no time flat he rigged up the PEG feeding machine to the plastic tubing so it hung behind and above me allowing me to feed whilst in the car. He's an ideas man, Murray, but then most farmers are.

Another neighbour and friend Alan Osborne also helped me with practical solutions. We were looking for a stand to hold the food and feeding machine but the medical ones were bulky and expensive. Alan saw a floodlight stand at Aldi that was portable and adjustable and he removed the lights and modified the pole to hold the equipment. Problem solved for $25. Alan also quickly modified my car-key because I did not have the strength to turn the key in the ignition.

Making the decision to have the PEG inserted was a big one for me. I think I was opposed to it because I saw how much my father hated it. However I had good advice from Dominic and the clinic dietician that I should consider doing this earlier rather than later. I had the tube inserted at Macquarie Hospital in August 2012 and although it was routine procedure I did not enjoy my stay. The worst thing was not being able to communicate and I determined I would do all I could to stay out of hospitals if I could. I recently found some diary notes of my stay and I think it is worthwhile to include my feelings at the time.

I knew I needed to go to Macquarie Hospital to have the PEG put in but I was not looking forward to it. Aside from the fact that it was an acceptance of the fact that I would soon be unable to eat, for some reason I was anxious about going in for the stay.

I had been a nurse and I was very familiar with a hospital environment and I had never been squeamish about having medical procedures. Clive, on the other hand, freely admitted that he was anxious about simple things like giving a blood sample. So I am not sure what exactly it was that was making me anxious.

Clive and I drove up and I was admitted and I hadn't been there long before I realised what the problem was. I had discussed with Dominic the various scenarios that faced me when I got near the end and a number of them ended with me in this hospital, never to leave.

I was having a preview of what could happen in a year or two when the MND had run its course. It was a stark confrontation with my own mortality and I was not prepared for it emotionally.

I had the operation and it was a bit more traumatic than I had expected with a fair bit of pain and I was held in intensive care for three days under observation. An ICU ward is all business with little scope for the niceties and I hated it there. The thing that most worried me was that I couldn't communicate properly because my speech was slurred and I was having difficulty engaging with the nursing staff. I remember a young nurse doing the rounds of the ICU came in to have a chat and when she realised how difficult it was to talk to me she made excuses and left quickly. It was 2 am and people were awake and in various states of pain and I lay there alone and vulnerable. It did not help to hear the same young nurse chatting away for ages to the young man in the next cubicle.

When Clive arrived early next morning he was shocked at how I was struggling but more so with how agitated I was being there. He was used to me getting on with things and became angry when he understood what had happened. I know hospitals are full of temporary nurses who are just covering for staff and so on but as an ex-nurse I could not understand that thoughtlessness.

I also had an interesting experience with a young registrar who was a budding neurologist getting some experience under Dominic's tutelage. He came and carried out his examination and asked questions about the progression of my MND. However I noticed he was not that engaged so I asked some questions about his interest in neurology. He said he didn't find MND that interesting because there was no cure and he preferred working in some of the other neurological diseases. This was fair enough but he was saying this to someone with MND and hadn't thought through how that might impact on them. I told Clive and he said I should give him some feedback. We had done a whole session on giving feedback when we ran the mentor course so I understood the process very well.

When he returned the next day I asked him if he managed to see many patients with Dominic and he said he did and Dominic was a very fine neurologist. I said to him "More importantly he is a very fine human being. He treats everyone with humanity and warmth. I think you are going to be a fine doctor but take the opportunity to watch and learn how Dominic treats his patients. Watch how he speaks to them and relates to them because this is what will make you a wonderful doctor". He was an intelligent young man and I think the penny dropped about his careless comment the day before. Hopefully he took it on board.

Clive and Emma could see I was struggling so between them they spent a lot of time at the hospital keeping me company. I told them to go and that I was OK but I was secretly very happy that they insisted on staying around.

What came out of this experience is that I would try and organise things so I did not spend my final days in this or any other hospital if I could help it. I don't mean to be over-critical because I know full well that the majority of medical staff are wonderful dedicated people. I just felt that I would prefer to be in my own environment when I died. I had no idea how this could be achieved but I was going to try.

It is an intrusive thing to have a hole in your body with a tube to feed through but for me it was a good decision made just in time. In only a few weeks it was very difficult for me to take food orally. The process of trying to eat was difficult and I risked choking fits as I tried to swallow.

The pleasure of eating was gone for me in any case and I quickly adapted to the practicality of getting the calories in the most efficient way possible. Initially I poured liquid down the tube through a syringe, including the odd glass of wine, but after some months this became time-consuming and tedious with the inevitable spills. I reluctantly agreed to the feeding machine which pumps in a prepared food at a very regulated rate. However despite my emotional reaction to being connected to a machine to eat, the feeding worked really well for me. I could feed at night, while sleeping and I was freed up during the day to get on with what I wanted to do.

There were always two ways to look at this MND progression and loss of function. You could concentrate and grieve the loss (in this case, independent eating) or you could solve the problem, accept the loss, and take advantage of the new freedom gained. I am not saying it was that simple for me but with the help of the dietician and my psychologist I moved onto PEG feeding with few regrets. My friends and family often felt guilty and embarrassed about eating and drinking around me. I think I was able to convey to people in the end, that, for me, that was a former part of my life and I now had other important things I wanted to do.

The medical professionals told me that people often wait too long to get the PEG and with MND it is easy to lose weight and condition quickly once you cannot get the nutrition. Once you lose weight it is hard to get it back as it takes so much time and effort to feed. I was fortunate this was not a problem for me and I believe the PEG gave me another twelve months of quality living.

I felt the loss of my speech terribly although it did not happen overnight. I gradually became more and more difficult to understand and of course this varied according to whom you were communicating with. My friend Lydia was able to understand me long after I became unintelligible to everyone else, including Clive. I am not sure why but I think it was a combination of her communication skills (she speaks three or four languages), her patience and being female. Anyway Lydia added MND-speak to her resume of languages and it was wonderful to be able to speak with her as long as I did.

However eventually I had to let go of oral communication as everyone, including me, was struggling with it. There are only so many times people say "sorry what was that" before it becomes obvious the time has come. The speech therapist told me when I stopped trying to speak there would be a sense of relief and she was right. I had not realised how much energy I was using trying to make myself understood.

I started using an electronic pad which was easy as you wrote and then erased and it could be carried anywhere. I then downloaded some software for my iPad that converted written word into speech. It was a clever program with a lovely voice that allowed me to have my say in a group conversation environment. However both of these aids could not cover the gap that occurred between when I had something to say and when it was communicated to the listener. Despite the very best intentions of people, often I would prepare a comment only to find the conversation had moved on to something else. It was OK one-on-one but nothing is the same as having your voice.

I even tried for a while to learn sign-language, which is contemporaneous and expressive but the problem is that it is like learning a new language and you can only communicate with someone who also knows it. In the end I did use a lot of sign language (some quite rude) between Clive and I but a lot of it was stuff we made up between us with no meaning beyond the two of us.

Finally I relied on a pad and pen to communicate. It was the simplest and best solution for me and I was lucky that I had good function in my hands for so long. I could express myself with the odd swear word, in capitals, and my close friends and family adapted to it very well. Interestingly, some people felt compelled to write down their responses even though I would point out to them I could understand their speech perfectly. It's a bit like people yelling at a blind man because they think he can't hear. One of the legacies I leave behind is box of notepads representing a year of conversations.

My favourite activities of recent years have been my perennial love of reading and movies, snorkelling with Clive and spear-fishing with him, my summer vegetable garden and making things with the produce. I still love to cook for Clive and friends even though I can't eat or actually try what I am cooking, so it is amazing when I am making up a dish from my head that it actually turns out.

I think that I may have had my last snorkel. I won't

have the energy or dexterity to do the vegetable garden again and even with the cooking I can't do it every day now. But I am reading a lot and watching movies and of course I have taken up writing in a limited way.

After a while you don't yearn for the functions that you have lost, you just adapt. What is harder for others to understand is that socialising just becomes too taxing and you start to withdraw into a smaller world. Even though I have an electronic speech program and can write on a pad, as I explained, in a social setting you are always too far behind the conversation, then you no longer see the point of commenting. I am not complaining, just explaining how it goes.

In my case I have lived a very full life since being diagnosed. Despite the rapid onset of bulbar MND to my upper body I have maintained capability in my limbs throughout. This meant I was able to travel and walk and swim without any impediment other than some fatigue. It also meant I have been able to look after my personal needs independently. MND patients can be in a wheel chair within three months of diagnosis and yet still be able to eat, drink and speak. I am not sure which situation I would prefer but I am not complaining about the way things have played out for me. Each type of MND presents its own challenges.

The MND association provided fantastic support to Clive and me but one thing I did not pursue was the meetings with fellow patients. I know the intent was to provide a forum for people with similar issues but they just did not work for me. I found it confronting to look around the room and see people in varying levels of progression. I decided it was better to not see too far into the future. Interestingly Dominics clinics were organised in such a way that you very rarely came face to face with other patients. I am sure there are plenty of people who would get great benefit out of the meetings but it just did not work for me.

Quite recently things have started to get a bit tougher. It is no longer easy for me to get enough nutrition through the, (PEG), tube. The excess saliva issue, which has plagued me from very early in the process, has now started to impact on me more critically. A day hardly passes when I don't get a choking cough that wracks my body and makes breathing difficult. I can reduce the coughing caused by mucous build-up low in my throat by not feeding but my body needs a litre of the formula food a day to survive. My time is coming.

The blessing is that I have had the time to tell my two sons how much I love them and how proud I am of the men that they have become. I have had some lovely times with them both, here in Narooma and in Darwin. I wish that I could have made it to London again to see Ash, as I like to have a picture in my mind of where he lives. It isn't easy to get to Narooma from Darwin, let alone London, but they have both made every effort to spend time with me and for that I thank them both.

On reflection I have had a pretty full life. My early childhood was quite happy, but my teens and up until Clive and I got together when I was forty, were pretty turbulent. Now having recently had my sixty-seventh birthday I am happy with the woman I have become. Anyway, I don't think I have too much time left to improve on the model.

I had a lovely email from David's wife Kate recently where she thanked me for my support and love and said that I had taught her a lot and that I had been a role model for her. I have been able to give the same support to Emma and Lisa and I know that they appreciate it.

I felt for Kate and Ryan coming to Australia having left their families and closest friends in North America. So I tried to look out for them as individuals, not just as daughters-in-law. I guess, having lived in China, I knew that even though we speak English here, there is a lot that is different culturally between Australia, USA and Canada. I was caught unaware with reverse culture shock when we came back to Australia after China. After two years Guangzhou had become our home. I even used to get ready to bargain in the shops!

I have been amazed at the love and kindness that has been constantly given to me throughout my journey with this illness. I have been given gifts to keep me warm, smelling nice, flowers to cheer me up, drawings from Emma's children, cards and photos and free facials. I get easy access to my GP Dr Jenny Wray and the allied health professionals from the Eurobodalla Community Health Service visit me at home. The pharmacist and her staff are also wonderful to me. One of the girls at the pharmacy lost her father to MND and she says that I am her favourite customer. We also have a wonderful psychologist in Lisa Freeman who keeps both Clive and me bolstered up.

I have become a hugger; it is a way to tell people they are important to me when I cannot speak. Friends (especially male friends) that would be reticent, have given me permission to hug when they might have been uncomfortable.

Margarets husband Bill Falls, the BFG (Big Friendly Giant), is the best example

When friends and family arrive they may not get a conversation but they will inevitably get a hug. It is another little bonus of my condition that people indulge me. It is an intimate act that has become a great comfort for me.

So: a message, people, don't wait to get MND, hug the people you love now.

CHAPTER 24

My Significant Other Clive and our Mate Buster

From before we were even an "item" Clive and I had a bond of friendship. He is intelligent, witty, kind and loyal. Those who know him well recognise that he is accident-prone and somewhat challenged on the domestic duties front. I have done some amazing clean-ups after some of his, oopsies. I am learning to be more patient about that aspect of his character as he genuinely tries to take on more domestic responsibility. He is my rock and homing beacon — the person I can always count on to be on my side.

We have been together now for twenty-six years, twenty-seven this October if I am still around. Right from the start Clive has seen potential in me that I never knew existed. He encouraged me to work at the airport doing immigration processing and encouraged me to apply for the China placement. If not for him I would never have lived and worked in China and never known such success.

When we got together we didn't have much wealth. I had furniture and a car. After his divorce settlement, which included sharing his superannuation and paying maintenance for the three children, Clive was left with some money invested in a house in Bendigo and his small yacht.

We managed to scrape together $9,000 for the deposit to buy a unit in Malak, Darwin, which we eventually sold seven years later for double the price we had paid for it. We bought the government house that we were renting in Wanguri and when we finally sold it we also made a profit. That allowed us to purchase the house in Leanyer, which offered us more space for the same amount that we got for the Wanguri house.

Clive had already started overtime doing Customs processing at the Darwin airport. With his encouragement I started doing the same for Immigration. We were both paying ten percent of our salary into our Commonwealth superannuation funds. I also did a few months of shift work at the airport, which had the effect of increasing my salary for superannuation purposes. I was not very good with financial matters except that I didn't live beyond my means but with Clive's financial acumen we did very well.

We were unable to sell the Leanyer house before we went to China so we rented it. We finally sold it in a falling market but it meant that we could get the costs of selling in Darwin and buying in Canberra reimbursed from my Department. Our forays into buying and selling real estate served us fairly well. On two occasions we sold the first day of the open house, that was the Wanguri house and the Canberra house. The people who bought Cooinda from us also decided to buy on a first viewing. We haven't been so lucky with the house in Gareth Avenue but we do have good tenants. Recently we sold one of the Darwin properties that we own with Nico and that was at the top of the Darwin market.

Together, Clive and I have made a good team. He has

a good feel for market trends and I know how to maintain a property and how to present it for sale. After we left Cooinda we formed our own company and began working with Nico training indigenous people to be mentors for other indigenous people just starting out in the workforce. Once again Clive convinced me that I could stand up in front of a group and present course content to participants. We would travel with Nico and do the courses together, but often it was just Clive and me working together. The last time I did that was August 2011 not long after I was diagnosed with MND.

After we built our "Grand Design" and moved in we also took on a couple of Nico's contracts in the local area. We had to assess and try to find work for indigenous people who had previously been participants on the Wallaga Lake Community Development Employment Programs (CDEP) which took us all the way down to Eden. Kate and David worked with us on this project and we were lucky that we had included a large study in the house from which we could work. Clive also managed a project in Moruya, but Carl, Ryan and an indigenous woman Bev Morton did all casework with the clients.

What this means to me is that I have more wealth than I would ever have achieved alone and that means I can leave some inheritance to my sons.

Clive has never wavered in his love for me, even though I now can't speak or eat a meal with him without drooling. His devotion knows no bounds. He still tells me every day that I am gorgeous and he loves me and that he doesn't see me as a sick person. That's pretty special.

He asked me recently what I really enjoy, given the fact that my life has become so limited. I told him I love seeing Buster do tricks so every day he runs through Buster's repertoire. He also knows how I love watching him play with Emma's children.

I have a theory based on my experience in relationships that most men need women in their life. But not all men really like women. They feel more comfortable in the company of other men. Hence the classic Aussie barbeque with all the men grouped together talking about sport and enjoying a beer. It is not a feminist rant or criticism, more an observation.

Clive really likes women. He has a special love and respect for women that I first observed with the way he treated his mother and sister, Margaret. This is a special quality and I know all my female friends like him. The women on the training courses we ran trusted him and revealed things about themselves that you would not expect in a five-day course. A man who loves and respects women makes a great lover and that is all I am going to say about that.

I didn't have a "bucket list" so he set about taking me on holidays with friends, mostly based around the sea and snorkelling in marvellous places. That is another skill that he taught me, snorkelling, to the extent that I became his spearfishing mate. Once again we worked very well together and worked out a good system so that we didn't lose too many fish. He built my confidence in the water and I felt so secure that I never had any fear of the water or anything in it.

At age forty I found my soul-mate. It will be tough

leaving him to live without me and for me to go alone on an unknown journey, without him to hold my hand. I hope he finds another person to love him and share the rest of his life with him. He deserves another shot at happiness. I do have a successor in mind who has been a friend of ours for years but I won't embarrass the poor woman by naming her in print. I have even written a reference for him for any potential future partners but he is very dismissive of this idea.

I think it is fair to say that we have never been more in love than in the last two years. Considering the circumstances of our life, with MND hanging over us like a black cloud, it is a wonderful thing.

He has given me a promise that he will be there beside me at the end and this provides me with a great sense of comfort.

In the meantime he will have his loyal mate Buster by his side. We didn't plan on getting another dog after our beloved Milo died but one day when we were in Bermagui, Clive saw an advert in a shop window for a dog that needed a good home. We followed up on the advert and went to take a look at him. He was on a property just out of Bermagui and was good mates with a horse there. Buster had been the guy Garry's daughter's dog in Sydney, but they had moved from a house into a unit and could no longer keep him. Garry took him to his property but he was planning to sell and move back to Sydney and wanted to find him a good home.

Garry wasn't prepared to let Buster go to just anybody so we got him on trial for a few days while Garry went to Sydney. If it didn't work out he would pick him up on the way back, however, it all went well. When we reported how it all went to Garry he said Buster was ours on the proviso that if anything went wrong we would call him first before offloading him elsewhere. That has never been an issue.

He is clever and Clive gets lots of pleasure from teaching him tricks. He is also a bit of a lap-dog and loves to snuggle up and in particular he loves to tuck his head under something. He is beloved by everybody who knows him. Doug and Lydia are like second parents and he gets the run of their place when they are in Narooma. He rushes to greet them when they arrive.

He also has a special bond with Andy Foster who taught him his first trick, which was to lie down to a command spoken in Russian! Andy always has treats for Buster and in times gone by when we would go there for drinks he would make a special plate of gourmet treats just for Buster.

His other great mates are Margaret and Alan who love him to bits and he loves them. It's no wonder because they spoil him. He has so many toys there to play with. Margaret in particular plays games with him all the time. They are only too keen to mind him for us if we go away and that is wonderful for us and for him. He even goes for the odd sleepover with them even when we are here. It is no wonder that he likes it there as he started out sleeping in his bed, then he graduated to sleeping on Alan's bed and now I hear that he actually sleeps in the bed; I know that to be true because he is always trying to get into bed with me and lie between my legs. If he has had a bath or I am going to change the sheets I let him into the bed, as it is both funny and comforting.

Buster has been a wonderful companion for both Clive and me and a great comfort when he snuggles up between us on the couch. He has been a welcome diversion from the situation that we face with my having MND. We are both glad that we got him. He has become a loved personality for the neighbourhood.

CHAPTER 25

A Surprise Party and Comments from Others

As an ordinary person with no special skills like being a renowned surgeon, an author, an actor, researcher or inventor, you don't expect to make any kind of mark in the world and of course I haven't. But the friends who were at my surprise sixty-seventh birthday party wanted to say a few things to me rather than as an obituary and that is very special.

I don't think that people should suddenly become saints because they have died so I am relying on all of my kids and Clive to talk of me as I really was. The cleaning tyrant, the bossy person, the one who threw potatoes at Clive, who left Paul a duster and said that it wasn't an artifact, who treated Ashley like a girl, picking him up from parties and who had to be finally told not to buy him any more T-shirts. The little picture person as Clive used to say. The one who sticks *domestic science* notes up all over the kitchen. So for a "shark" personality I have done well to be held in such high regard by my friends.

Clive said he worked for weeks organising a surprise birthday party for me, even down to arranging for someone to mind Hannah so Emma could come down a day early, and not only bring Max as planned, but my special baby Ava.

Doug and Lydia, Marg and Alan plus Lisa, Carl and Ryan prepared the main meal out of sight from me. Other friends brought snacks and sweets and, as luck would have it, I was trying out a gluten-free chocolate orange cake, a Nigella Lawson recipe which came in handy. The party organizers kept saying to Clive, "Do you think she knows?, she must!" but he was sure that I didn't and he was right, it was a complete surprise.

So thank you, my dear Clive, for all of the hard work and, most of all, the love that you put into the arrangements. I never know what you are going to arrange for me next. You have certainly invented a bucket list of events for me that have been wonderful.

Birthday Message from Doug Woodhouse

18 June 2013

Written and delivered by Doug Woodhouse
(with oversight by Lydia Morton)

We did not want to celebrate your birthday and not let you know how we feel about you. So what follows is a very brief outline of those feelings.

We think of all the wonderful aspects of your personality and, in particular, the Cheryl who brings so much joy to those of us who have been lucky enough to be able to consider you a close friend and mate.

We see your unconquerable spirit, a spirit that lets you meet your challenges with great courage, honesty, dogged persistence and genuine dignity. It is a spirit that has seen you through the most difficult of times as you travelled, and continue to travel, the highway of life and, it is a spirit that we who know you acknowledge with unabashed respect.

We admire your sensitivity as you see needs in others that are often not seen by us and we appreciate the way you quietly respond to those needs with your soft touch and gentle understanding. It is an understanding that comes from the heart, based on wisdom, life experiences, wise judgment and an inner strength that you, Cheryl ,have in great abundance!

We respect and treasure your uniqueness and we feel honoured to know such an extraordinary and truly beautiful person. We all agree that there is no one else like you.

Cheryl, on this special of birthdays, we want you to know that we cherish you for whom and what you are and that we love you.

Happy birthday!

Cheryl's Birthday Speech
Read by Carl Broman

I don't know how I have been so lucky to have such wonderful family and friends.

You have all helped me in many ways to make my life with MND more bearable.

I am not extraordinary or particularly brave; in the end you just make the best of it.

Laughter and tears help a lot. The laughter buoys my spirits and the tears clear the air.

This quote appealed to me when I read it .

> *"And did you get what you wanted*
> *from this life, even so?*
>
> *I did*
>
> *And what did you want?*
>
> *To call myself beloved,*
> *to feel myself beloved on the earth.*
>
> - Raymond Carter

And dear friends I have been beloved by Clive, our six children and all of you.

I will die a happy person.

CHEZZA

CHAPTER 26

Sudden Death of
my Little Brother

Since I started writing this story my brother Brian has died, and quite suddenly. He was only fifty-eight and although he was being treated for lung cancer there was no evidence to suggest that he would die suddenly. He was in hospital to treat an abscess, also in his lung, and had a massive hemorrhage and died within minutes.

As I said earlier we had never been close but we became closer since we both took ill around the same time. I was surprised at how distraught I felt at his death but then memories came flooding back of when he was little and I so often took care of him. I had expected that I would go first and that he may have had a chance to beat the cancer or at least to have had more time to spend with his three children and grand-daughter. I had been sorting out family photos and documents that I thought he would like to have, ready for our planned catch-up at the end of July.

I never expected to be the last of my Moon family. But as my neurologist Dominic says, none of us knows when our time will be up.

Clive and I were driving to Sydney on the day he died, to fly to Darwin to see Paul. Ashley was also flying into Darwin for a week and we were all attending their cousin's wedding. We of course changed our plans and even Ashley did too, flying into Canberra via Melbourne so he could attend the funeral with us. It was a great comfort to me to have him there and he read my eulogy and one from him and Paul.

Brian's oldest, Kelly, did most of the organising of the funeral. She was working part-time, taking care of her toddler Sienna and yet still found the time to keep me informed of what she was planning. On the day, Kelly, Phillip and Sarah all spoke about their Dad and he would have been so proud of them. They and Sienna were his life.

Clive, Ashley and I went to Darwin together and got there in time to attend Michael Fong's wedding. It was lovely to see my boys with their cousins, father and their young half- brother Saul, aunts and uncles. This was such a wonderful family event and so humbling to be treated as an integral part of the Fong family. I stayed at this wedding well beyond my expectations but I have a suspicion it will be my last significant social event.

It was also good to be there in Darwin when Brian's son Phillip came back from Wagga, so that we could give him some family support.

Ashley left after only four days in Darwin. It was hard for me to say goodbye and also later to Paul as I never know if it is the last time that I will see them. If it is I am happy in the knowledge that they know how much I love them. I was not a perfect mother (who is really?) but I don't think that they have ever doubted my love and interest in them.

The problem with the feeding persists and I have

arranged to go into Macquarie University Hospital for assessment and to see if we can stabilise a feeding regime. A bonus will be that I should get to see the new MND research centre.

On the deck at Iolandas and Juergens Sydney 2012.

Lars visiting from Germany in 2012 with Ash at Mystery

My great friend Andy giving me a hug in the galley of the yacht
on our Whitsunday holiday.

The motley crew sailing our magnificent 53 foot charter boat (Deanna, Lydia, Doug W, Andy, Jethro at the wheel, me, Carol

Lydia my friend on a beach in the Whitsundays.

Snorkelling in Bora Bora my favorite holiday place.

Resting with another bear at Emmas 2013.

A good seasons production summer 2012.

Lisa and I in the kitchen Christmas 2011.

Paul visiting in summer of 2012.

Carl and Ryan partying on the deck Christmas 2011.

Witness at Dave and Kate's wedding 2013.

After a dive with Emma and Ava looking on 2013.

Ash with me at Sorrisos, on one of his many visits from London,
after he knew of my MND diagnosis

My friend Matt doing fundraising for MND 2012.

Clive, Buster and I July 2013.

A successful catch of fish after a dive in Narooma.

Buster the Carer

A deserted beach in the Whitsundays 2012

Cheryl's great friend Marg Falls who looked after her till the very end

CHAPTER 27

Your Partner Has His Say, by Clive Broman

It has been a fantastic experience reading your story because it doesn't matter how well you think you know someone, there is always more to learn. I know you see it as an ordinary life and, whilst that may be true, in the grand scheme of things it is still an important story to be told.

Everyone has a story and I think someone said once that an important role of a partner is to be a witness to one's life. It has been a pleasure to be a witness to yours. Whilst this book tells much of the life you have lived it's nice to know that there are still some things (like the Tioman Monkey) that are still yet to be told.

I know we have never revealed the Tioman Monkey story to many people but it is probably worthy of a run, given how much of a laugh we got out of it.

We had arrived in Tioman at our hotel and it was a delightful place, very close to the beach and yet jungle coming up to the very edge of the hotel buildings.

We had seen the warnings about not feeding the monkeys, as they could be quite aggressive, so when we walked to the beach we were careful not to let them get too close.

We had a lovely swim in the gorgeous waters and made our way back to the hotel for a rest in the afternoon. We relaxed and had some wine and nibbles. It was certainly a romantic environment and of course one thing led to another and and next thing we are on the couch, when suddenly you say to me, "Somebody's watching us". I always thought you were a little paranoid about stuff like that but then sure enough, we looked up and there was a monkey sitting on the coffee table eating the nibbles and observing these other mating primates with a bemused look on his face.

He was quite stubborn about leaving the premises but when I did finally get him out the window I looked around and you had skedaddled to the bedroom. Alas, that was the end of any monkey business for that day.

It's been an amazing journey. I still wonder at times how I managed to pull it off. Spending my life with you. We were the garden gnome and the princess.

Talking of the garden gnome, let me start with a poem based on my first impressions

'FIRST IMPRESSIONS'

She moved with a steady determined grace.
Like many women of beauty
She seemed unaware or her impact.

The shoulders straight, she seemed taller than she was,
More tough times than easy had given her a strength and a fragility.

She spoke with private-school eloquence, but no airs.

Was it a severity or just that "singlemother" seriousness that comes with the need to get it done day after day, every day?

If she looked you in the eye and put her hands on her hips, LOOK OUT!

Next she was flaring the nostrils and it's time to flee, but could she maintain it if you made her laugh?

And when she did laugh, a lifetime of responsibility would melt away to reveal the delightful woman beneath.

I knew she was interesting,
I knew I liked her and enjoyed our moments,

What I didn't realise was that I had fallen in love with her.

You have been the reason for the most courageous decision of my life. It was a fork in the road that required me to choose love over so many other things.

There was the excitement of a new passion but there was also so much more than that. How could I have known that what lay ahead was going to provide so much more meaning to my life and yours? I was able to show you something in yourself that you hadn't seen before. It was obvious to me, your strength of character – it just wasn't obvious to you.

I wasn't quite sure what you saw in me but I know my mother understood how you recognised it and appreciated you for it. What a discovery to find such strongly-held core values- from social justice to Easter eggs on Good Friday – united by atheism. That is an amazing aspect of our relationship. There were other things, a passion for travel and a genuine interest in meeting people from different cultures and walks of life.

If you consider our professional lives we were equals throughout our careers – at the same level – and in fact both promoted to management positions on the same day. But more than that there was enormous mutual respect for each other's professional behaviour and standards even before we were a couple. I think this is unusual for couples (Doug and Lydia have it) but it is not that common. I remember you saying to someone that I snuck under your guard because you saw me as a great mate.

We had reasonably successful careers and we always backed each other, unconditionally. Just as well, as there were times we were very much on our own. I take some pride in the fact that I pushed you in your career and in particular to apply for an overseas post. Sure, I was keen to live overseas even if I did it on your coat-tails but I saw the potential in you to succeed. Then I watched you outperform people with a lot more experience. It was a fantastic professional performance except for the brief period when you had to supervise me. I will admit to being somewhat recalcitrant as an employee but the problem was resolved by me heading off to manage the Austrade Office.

There is no doubt the major area of difficulty for us was in domestic science. Apparently you had gained a "Ph D" by the time you were 14 and I never really got out of kindergarten. I do admit to a lack of genuine enthusiasm or as a daughter of mine once said "my skills lie in other areas". I realised quite recently what I was up against when your cousin told me how astounded she was to visit you in Wonthaggi and at fourteen years of age you were running the whole house. It's tough to imagine, how that level of responsibility at such a young age affects you for the rest of your life. I did try, in fits and starts, but I was an ongoing disappointment and I apologise for that. I had other strengths but I should have been better. I now feel with notes in the kitchen that I am on the right track. It also helps that rigorous supervision has dropped off to some extent.

I can never thank you enough for what you did for my kids. I was pretty naive about how difficult it would be blending a family of five kids whilst embarking on a new relationship. You looked after their physical needs in a way that I couldn't and you provided them with standards that they still live by today. I did my best to give your two boys another source of support and provide a role model in areas where you had struggled. It was a difficult time as the domestic work had to get done, we both had busy jobs and the kids were all trying to adapt to a new situation. But as they grew you started to become an important person in their lives who they knew cared about them. They responded to that over time and are better adults because of you. They also have genuine affection and respect for you now, which is something that is not always achieved even by the biological parents.

In recent years it has been lovely to watch you reflect with some pride about the decent people that our children have become – along with their partners. A wonderful memory for me is your speech at Christmas 2011 where you made it clear (despite the MND slurring) how proud you were of them all.

I believe a change came over our relationship after our

marriage – not because of it but because of the timing. At the time it seemed a sensible thing to do to coincide with your fiftieth birthday. (I was so proud of how great you looked for a woman of fifty.). The wedding came about not long after we had lost our parents and the kids were all entering young adulthood. So it was in some ways our time and I think we started to understand that. We realised that we did love spending time together and there were lots of adventures out there to experience.

If you consider what we achieved around this time, both professionally and financially, we have much to be satisfied with. Through hard work (overtime at the airport), good financial planning and good decision-making we managed to move to a very sound financial situation. Given we started off in 1987 with virtually nothing, this was an impressive achievement. This was capped off by the decision to resign from the Public Service and buy Cooinda Apartments in Narooma, which eventually gave us a lot of freedom to travel and even build our own "Grand Design". It also will leave a legacy to our kids, which is something you and I never received.

We were able to indulge the passion for travel we both shared in the years after our marriage. It probably started off in Bali in our early trips where we loved the water and warm weather and were both pretty good swimmers. But our relationship went to another level when we started to snorkel together. I believe your interest also stemmed from not wanting to see me dive on my own. You were tentative at first as you got used to the equipment but because you lacked any fear of the water there was no stopping you.

You were such an enthusiastic support diver that the

spearfishing became even more enjoyable for me, as we worked together so well as a team. The moment I fired the gun I could sense you on my right shoulder with the float and the spike to get that fish on the wire. I will never forget a diving trip at Kangaroo Island when we were spearing these 6 kg monster drummers. They were so powerful they led us a merry dance as we tried to get them under control – we lost three in a row. You came to the surface and said, "I think we might be fighting over our weight limit". We both laughed and left them to the sea. These days when I dive without you I miss you more than you can imagine.

You were courageous and reliable and backed me up even in some quite scary situations. We shared a meaningful experience when we helped Doug Woodhouse out on a difficult day at Glasshouse Rocks.

Ashley gave us this wonderful gift of a trip to Bora Bora in 2010 and we would never have indulged in such an experience without his prompting and generosity. I still remember you walking into that over-the-water bungalow looking at the window in the floor and the fish below and bursting into tears.

I cannot imagine anything more exciting or memorable than the times we have shared in the water at Ningaloo Reef, Bora Bora, and Lady Elliott Island and, of course, our favorite spots around Narooma. How wonderful swimming along and reaching back to feel your hand in mine. It is a joyous thing to share together – I am not saying it's better than sex but it's close.

You have done a pretty good job describing the MND journey and it seems a miserable way to finish a story and a life. But like all experiences of adversity there is a silver lining. I have read books about people living with adversity and life-ending illnesses and they are always full of inspirational stuff about how they are better people and have learnt so much about life because of their experience. To be honest I did not really see much to celebrate watching my partner deal with the inexorable progression of MND.

We had so many things that we still wanted to do together and why shouldn't we have had that opportunity like all our friends and relatives around us. I wasn't bitter or angry but I wasn't exactly thrilled with the situation either. It was difficult not to feel a little cheated. However things started to change as we came to terms with what lay in front of us. It was obvious that the MND curse also opened up some special experiences.

What a privilege it was to meet and then become friends with Professor Dominic Rowe and his staff who always treated us with respect and affection and drew us into his passion to beat, as he calls it, "this fucking disease." How satisfying it was to be able to make a really meaningful contribution to the emerging MND Research Centre at Macquarie Uni with the help of Ashley's employer Macquarie Bank. Then, on visiting those brilliant people to see how dedicated and motivated they were to discover the mysteries of MND. I was left in no doubt that this group would someday defeat this disease.

Would we really have become such close friends with Doug and Lydia and then travelled to Bora Bora with them if it wasn't for MND? Would we have flown to Ningaloo with Bruce and Jan or Norfolk Island with

Iolanda and Juergen?

It's difficult to imagine that motley crew of people putting aside their priorities and heading off to the Whitsundays to sail a 53-foot boat if they had not been motivated to do so by your situation.

I am convinced that the relationship you had with your boys went to a level that would never have been achieved under normal circumstances. It is difficult to put a value on that. Parents go through their whole lives without really connecting with their kids as they would hope. MND put aside any reticence that stood in the way of your boys letting their mother know what they thought of her. I noticed that with all the kids that the child/parent relationship matured overnight and they all wanted to do what they could to help. Then of course there was Emma giving you the special gift of Ava on top of the wonderful relationship we had with Hannah and Max. I can't help but feel this happened for a reason and gave you so much joy at a difficult time.

Time and again I have listened to people say that they have changed their priorities and values because they observed our situation. The most common theme is they no longer sweat the small stuff. Well, for you and me, that has become a lifestyle and our relationship is so much gentler and respectful than it has ever been or perhaps ever would have been. The time you revealed to our psychologist that, as you were going through old photos of ours and sorting things out, you felt like you were falling in love with the "garden gnome" again, was one of the most delightful feelings I can remember. Interestingly I was having exactly the same feelings about you, but more so because I was so proud of the way you handled the progression of your MND.

Only someone who gets the diagnosis of a disease like MND can understand what's involved. It's not about being brave because, as you said, you don't get a choice really. So the test of character is in how you adapt and this is where you came up trumps.

For someone with your attributes, MND seemed to be an especially cruel disease. You were always so beautifully presented and well spoken but MND in your case started with the slurring speech and then the constant excess saliva. The way you dealt with this viscous attack on your person was both determined and practical as you maintained your dignity, your humour and your presentation despite enormous challenges. This is not a fanciful opinion of mine: it is backed up by many independent comments to that effect from your doctors, friends, relatives etc. It demonstrated to me how a person with genuine grace and beauty can never be brought down.

I can recall so many times seeing you exhausted and drawn in bed and then you would get yourself up and appear down those stairs with the red or the aqua or a new scarf and be "take-my-breath-away-gorgeous". I am madly in love with you so I could be seen as biased but there were plenty of others who were astounded at how you managed this.

You are a great cook and enthusiastic dinner party entertainer and MND took away your ability to eat. Yet you kept cooking and you continued to grow your vegetables and delight in a new cake recipe to share with others. If that does not demonstrate an exceptional quality

I am not sure what does.

You are a great communicator and commentator on life and important social and political issues but MND took away your ability to speak. You struggled bravely to speak long after it became too hard then switched to an electronic pad and an iPad speech program. Finally you decided that a pen and pad was the go – you always had nice writing – and filled hundreds of these pads in patient, witty and sometimes, profane scribblings. You have managed to remain relevant to any conversation. Our close friends noticed that as you became annoyed (mainly with me) the writing became bigger and more profane. I knew how frustrating and exhausting it was and how easy would it have been to just bow out.

You also took to SMS and email with a genuine enthusiasm, which was mostly motivated by helping and guiding others, particularly our kids and Emma. When I saw some of the SMS traffic between Ashley and you, it was clear what a change had occurred for you both. The iphone has done its job to put you on equal terms with your friends and family.

Despite all these wonderful things that have occurred since April Fools Day 2011, I would still rather be facing a life together without MND as we were poised for some fun times after some tough ones. But I cannot complain with the life I have had in these last two years because it has made me appreciate every moment we spend with each other.

The sad irony of this situation is that you are a natural carer and would do the job I am trying to do so much more competently. You have looked after me for twenty-seven years and if our positions were reversed we would both be managing better. Despite your MND, whenever I needed help, like when I tore my quad muscle, you have stepped up to look after me despite your own problems. Now as this dreadful disease progresses and you struggle with the basics, like getting nutrition in some sort of comfort, I feel so helpless. I know there is often nothing I can do but I suspect if it was me, you would find a way to help.

Each day we both face another challenge as MND never gives you anything back or offers any respite. We know the unspoken future and deal with it as best we can. The important thing is we face these things together with our good friends and doctors, Dominic Rowe and Jenny Wray, there to help when we really need it.

MND will continue to take away your capacity day by day and is relentless. It tears at my heart as I watch it. But it can't stop our growing love and only we know how special that has been in the face of this onslaught.

There will be a time when we say goodbye and I know we prepare ourselves in ways that acknowledge the end is near. I know you worry about me, and the life I might have after you are gone. You are convinced that I will always need someone in my life but I might surprise you. Whatever happens, the place you occupy in my life will always be there to provide me with a smile and a tear when I need it.

You were my friend, my wife, my lover for over twenty seven years. Of all these the most important was friendship which is based on compatible intellects and shared values.

Life with you has been a wonderful journey. It has

been an extraordinary privilege to have shared the most important part of my life with you my love.

Goodbye my lover, goodbye my friend.
My life goes on but my love wont end.

Clive Broman

CHAPTER 28

The Final Chapter

The desperate trip to Sydney to try and resolve the feeding problems has failed.

My doctor has visited and the options are bleak. If I continue to feed I will choke and suffocate. Each time it happens and Clive or Doug pound me on the back while I try to suction the stuff from my throat, I get exhausted.

The idea that I was reacting to the type of feed proved wrong as the result is the same, no matter what I use. It is in my living will and I have stopped the feeding and my doctor will try and keep me comfortable for as long as it takes. I knew this time would come and I am ready for it.

I have sent the word out to London, Darwin, Melbourne and Canberra and my kids have descended on me to say goodbye.

I know now my time is up but what a joy to have my boys Ash and Paul with me. My step-children Lisa and Carl have been here with their partners Lachie and Ryan helping out and supporting Clive. And of course my adopted daughter Emma in the thick of it providing her love and support.

My wonderful friend Marg Falls has set up camp in the house with a view to seeing this through to the end, very brave Marg and such a comfort. And of course my adopted daughter Emma in the thick of it providing her love and support.

I could not have hoped for a better way to spend these

last days in my beautiful home with Doug and Lydia next door and being watched over by marvellous professionals Steph Ratcliffe and Dr Jenny Wray.

This last communication is done with the help of my partner Clive right alongside me as he promised. Despite his doubts he turned out to be a wonderful carer. I love you, darling.

Farewell, readers. I hoped you enjoyed my ordinary story.

Chezza

06/09/13

EDITORS NOTE

Cheryl Fong died 09/09/13 after refusing any more feed and eventually fluid, but was relaxed and comfortable in the end. Her heart pounded strongly for a long time and was obviously unaffected by the MND.

She spent her last coherent hours giving comfort and support to those she left behind. Her last note to me was "I feel like I am abandoning you".

Professor Dominic Rowe contacted me within minutes of her death and made the observation that she had managed MND as well as anyone he had seen. He also reaffirmed his promise to beat this "fucking" disease.

A memorial service was held at her home in Narooma attended by her many friends and family. Her good mate Lydia Morton delivered the eulogy and another friend Ruth Perret delivered Cheryl's own farewell. Both of these speeches are in the appendices. My life-long friend Rob (Arra) Millen who was involved in both my weddings delivered my message to Cheryl as I knew I would struggle to get it done.

Cheryl's old indigenous friend Tom Calma, who first knew her as nurse Moon back in 1964 sent her an email a few days before she died in which he remembered their friendship. He concludes with:

"As the moon rises we wish you a long and peaceful journey swimming with the whale sharks and seals and giant rays; just

drifting in the serenity of an ebbing tide along the boardwalk as you did so many times with Alice while we walked on the deck and watched you float towards the horizon. We love you, Cheryl, and each month as we witness the birth of the new moon and watch it grow into the fullest and brightest moon we will be thinking of you, our true and loving friend. Love, Tom"[2]

Her children did a group snorkel at Glasshouse Rocks in Narooma (her favourite snorkelling spot). Within a few minutes of scattering Cheryl's ashes a whale drifted within 50 metres of shore to the amazement of all those present. Tom's wishes seemed to be fulfilled. She could not have hoped for a better farewell.

---

2 To view full message from Tom Calma, see Appendices

CHAPTER 29

A Few Observations from an Unlikely Carer

This is Cheryl's book so I have been careful about having too much to say. She asked me to write my own chapter. "Your Partner has his say". I was happy to do this because it gave me a chance to put down, for all to see, my admiration for her. As the book moved from a letter to her boys to a broader story with a wider audience it became obvious to me and other people who helped in the editing, that there was a potential audience of people dealing with MND. To that end I helped reorganise a lot of material to develop the chapter "Living with MND" so that it might provide useful information for newly diagnosed sufferers and their families.

I was asked by people at Macquarie University and MND Association of New South Wales to consider putting down my experience as a carer. It was also important to record our journey from diagnosis to Cheryl's death.

Anyone reading the book will understand that the carer role did not sit that well with me. But, like Cheryl, I did not really get a choice in the matter. I was anxious and a little frightened about whether I would cope. Early on I discussed my concerns with a good mate of mine, Bruce, who is pretty much a straight shooter, he listened and then simply said, "Well, it looks like you are going to have to step up." It was what I needed because, whatever way you looked at it there was no one else better placed to do the job.

I was lucky in that I had someone like Cheryl with a positive attitude and our team of medical professionals gave us very good support, but still, much depended on how we approached this dreadful situation as a couple. The day she was formally diagnosed we ended up catching up with friends and drinking champagne and laughing and crying together. This involvement with good friends set the tone for the way we both coped with the progression of the disease. I was open to people helping me and I think this was the key to managing, as our friends embraced the reality of our journey and seemed determined to participate as well as offering whatever help they could.

We did not feel like people were sorry for us, but more that they wanted to be involved and I think the secret here was to invite people to join us in the journey. As a consequence we had some wonderful trips with our friends who re-organised their lives to join us. I can honestly say that I believe this was not done out of sympathy or a sense of obligation because Cheryl made it clear she was able to approach these trips with an emphasis on fun, excitement and friendship. There was never any great discussion about what a terrible future lay ahead; it was very much about the here and now.

I think I managed to squeeze as much as I could out of the travel bucket list and it was worth the effort.

I had imagined a difficult time with managing Cheryl's progression, dealing with all the medical appointments etc. and looking after her daily needs as she lost capacity.

Well, there was all of that but that was not my main role. The most important thing I did was to continue our relationship as normally as possible. I don't think anyone wants to be, "cared" for, if they can avoid it and Cheryl was adamant about that from the very start. Of course that changes as you lose capacity. Cheryl wanted me to be a husband, lover and friend first and a carer second. I tried to do this to the very end by spending a lot time with her, talking about our friends and family and maintaining an intimate relationship with lots of affection and attention to each other's needs. I never slept in another bed despite the fact that there were issues and difficulties that would disturb my sleep. Cheryl tried to convince me that I needed to have a break and sleep elsewhere but I thought it was important to let her know I was going to be there through thick and thin, or in sickness and in health, if you want to refer back to the marriage vows. The title of Cheryl's book said it all and I think for someone with a terminal illness it's so important to know you are loved each day. I am not pretending this can be the case for everyone but I know how important it was for both of us dealing with the dark times.

I received the Carer Manual from the MND association and it was a valuable reference to have. I found, however, that it was not the sort of document you needed to read from cover to cover. In fact it could be quite disturbing if you did that. I used the manual to deal with issues as they arose rather than think about all the likely negative scenarios. MND is such an individual journey for people that you need to really focus on how things actually unfold for you rather than worry about what might occur.

For example, the major issue for us looked like being the unsuitability of our house. It was on four separate levels with stairs everywhere and the prospect of making it wheelchair friendly was very daunting. Cheryl made a decision, which she stuck to throughout, that she did not want to ruin her beautiful house.

We were aware that we had to have an alternative plan if Cheryl lost mobility but a friend, Andy Finlay, offered to lend us his holiday apartment in Narooma which was on one level. We had a back-up plan so we no longer worried about having to do major renovations. As it turned out, Cheryl stayed mobile and made her way down the stairs to join everyone at dinner a couple of days before she died.

The MND association encouraged carers to have some respite by funding a holiday break. This was a wonderful program because it was not just about the money, it was there to encourage people to plan for a change in the day-to-day routine. It was also important for developing the mindset of doing special things now, not at some time in the future. The most useful role I played in my caring role was the organising of little adventures that I knew Cheryl would enjoy without trying to push her beyond her steadily diminishing capacity.

The reality is that for all sorts of reasons you cannot go from one exciting adventure to another just because you have a terminal illness. We were lucky as we had the financial ability to pay for some great holidays but there was still a lot of time in between where you just lived a daily existence. I set myself a goal to try and do something each day that would bring pleasure to Cheryl and me. It was not that hard in the end, you just had to keep in mind that each day was precious and could not afford to be wasted. Towards the end when Cheryl was really struggling I asked her every week or so to write down five things that she got pleasure out of. I tried to deliver on these wishes and it became a fun thing, like teaching Buster a new trick that he could show off to her, or watching an old favourite movie.

A psychologist will talk about providing emotional support and I think the carer plays such an important role here. A loving partner is in a unique position to do this because they are closer than anyone else. I made it my mission to give positive feedback whenever I could. This doesn't work if it is not genuine but this never proved a problem for me. MND attacks a person in so many obvious ways, that it is easy for them to become despondent and feel embarrassed in public. I always acknowledged when Cheryl made the effort to present herself as well as she did. I told her daily that she was doing well and looked good and although she took this with a grain of salt, I know it gave her confidence to continue to put herself out there. I remember reading somewhere you cannot give a woman too much flattery or give a dog too many biscuits. Buster agrees.

I encouraged her to continue to buy nice clothes and things for herself, as she had always done, to avoid the idea of it being wasted because of what lay ahead. She embraced this concept and even brought some gorgeous expensive new glasses that we both knew she would probably only use for a few months. It was worth it for the boost it gave her the first time she wore them out. She even brought new saucepans a week before she died because she knew the old ones had had their day. I took them into the bedroom to unwrap them in front of her and Ashley used them to cook a big meal for the family that same week. It sounds silly but she got pleasure out of that.

During the MND journey there are frequent decisions for the person to make and some of these are very difficult emotionally. I always tried to help in that process by understanding the issues. This meant I went to all appointments, researched the various options and then was in a position to be a sounding board for Cheryl when it came to the decision time. For example when she was thinking of getting the PEG I talked to the doctors and dieticians and then encouraged her to look at the benefits rather than focus on the negatives. We made the decision together to go to Sydney for the operation and Emma and I stayed with her in intensive care as much as we could because we knew she felt so vulnerable.

After she started feeding through the PEG I learnt how to assist her in the day-to-day battle to get the calories in. Sometimes that required a little encouragement to set up the feed and get the machine running. If she was just sick to death of putting the prepared feed (or muck, as she came to call it) down the PEG I would try and substitute with a cold pressed juice or some Staminade. This was really just dealing with her emotional reaction and was not an alternative to the balanced feed but it would get her through a low patch. I never pushed her or lectured her about getting the calories in but she was OK with my encouragement.

It is important with MND to be honest and realistic

about where you are going with this disease. The fact is people, on average, die within two to three years and if you try and deny that reality there is a good chance you will miss opportunities to enjoy the time you have. Cheryl and I did not get caught up in false hope and miracle cures, even though there were a few on offer, and this allowed us to take advantage of the time we had. I have seen people who cannot accept that their partner is dying, refuse to discuss it or plan for it, and I don't believe that is very helpful at all. It is just as big a problem if the person who is ill does not accept what is unfolding for them.

I have mentioned in my chapter that our relationship got better and that was such a wonderful thing for us both. This is not always the case for carers and the people they care for, as anger, resentment, guilt and frustration can start to dominate the relationship. The key for us was to take time to communicate what was going on with each other and despite the fact that we were both reasonable communicators this would not have been possible without our psychologist, Lisa Freeman, providing fantastic support. Cheryl visited Lisa regularly and I would join her every couple of visits. Towards the end I starting seeing Lisa on my own and still do.

Despite all this support there were still times when one or the other of us would get frustrated or angry and lash out but we never let it stay an issue for long as we did not want to waste time. We made it a rule to never go to sleep at night without resolving any issues of the day.

I would advise anyone facing a tough time such as we did to seek support through a mental health plan from your GP; it is not a sign of weakness to do so.

There was one task that I was not prepared for and that was responding by phone and email to the constant stream of enquiries from friends and family about how Cheryl was doing. People were obviously concerned and interested but I don't think they understood how emotionally draining it was to do this, especially after Cheryl could no longer talk for herself. I discussed this with Lisa and we came up with a strategy to manage this which people eventually understood.

I started doing group email updates, and had an efficient and polite way to shorten phone calls.

One of the big causes of disagreement between us was the maintenance and management of the house. We have a lovely house and you will understand from Cheryl's background why she was so house-proud. I realized in the end she was getting frustrated because she could no longer do the work the way she wanted. I was never going to be able to do it to a suitable standard so we had to come up with a compromise. We were lucky we had a lovely woman named Sue doing the cleaning and eventually Cheryl was able to let her take more responsibility. Cheryl also came up with a great idea to leave notes in the kitchen explaining to me exactly how the kitchen cleaning should happen. It was clever because I had no excuses and she did not have to repeat herself. The notes are still there (laminated) and I find them very useful.

As Cheryl came close to the end, my carer role became more intense and more critical. I told people honestly if she was not up to a visit and would ring friends and tell them to come around if she was doing OK. I managed Cheryl more directly by ensuring she rested and did not try to work around the house. I called on friends to come and help with things that needed doing and also to help her sort out things she wanted to do before she was gone. In the last week of her life when her general condition went down so rapidly I put a large photo of her above her bed so people could have a lasting picture of the beautiful woman she had been. Many people, including the attending medical professionals, were touched and a little inspired by this and her family and friends thought it was a wonderful thing to see when you visited her. I think she was quite happy with the idea as well.

There is a strong view that carers need to take care of themselves and I think this is true. I did this as best I could by trying to exercise and keep healthy but I never felt a desperate need to get away from Cheryl or the house for any length of time. Many people suggested I should, and offered to stay with her while I took a break. It just did not feel right for me and in the end I think it was a selfish thing on my part that I did not want to spend time away from her when time together was so precious. I would have plenty of time to myself in the future but now it was important to be close by, even if we just sat together and didn't speak.

If you are caring for someone with MND or in fact any terminal illness, my advice is, don't think too far ahead. Seize the moment and if you have something you would like to do with your partner, do not put it off. Be kind to each other and be honest with each other. Accept the help of others and ask if you need it as most people are very grateful for the chance to contribute. Remember to always focus on the life you are living in that hour and that day and leave the future to unfold.

Cheryl and I had a bit of a thing for Whitney Houston and she sings a song called "You'll never stand alone", It could qualify as a Carers Anthem.

If there's a time when the tears should fill your eyes
And you can't see past the shadows to the sun on the other side
Don't despair, because there always will be someone there
Don't lose faith, love won't let you lose your way, because

You, you'll never stand alone, I'll be standing by
I'll keep you from the cold, I'll hold you when you cry
I'll be there to be strong when you can't find the strength inside
And you, you'll always have a home in these arms of mine
You'll never stand alone, love is standing by [3]

To know you are loved and not alone counts for a lot.

I have mentioned earlier how important intimacy was for both of us until the very end. Cheryl had the final say on this. We had just arrived back from Sydney after the fruitless trip to try and solve the feeding problem. I was still hopeful of a solution and had ordered several different types of food to see if we could find one that Cheryl could get down through the tube without resulting in the choking reaction.

I think Cheryl knew better than me that the end was not far away. Anyway she appeared out of the shower wrapped in a towel and handed me a note that said "I just want to feel normal again for a little while". I wasn't quite sure what she meant and then she dropped the towel and smiled at me.

---

3 excerpt taken from *elyrics.net*

It was such a brave performance given how vulnerable she felt in her failing body but she looked terrific and I told her so. We both knew this was a goodbye to a grand love affair that had lasted twenty-seven years. We had cried together many times on the MND journey but never with more awareness of the importance of the moment.

The next day Cheryl's doctor, Jenny Wray, came to visit to discuss the way forward. I thought I was ready to deal with the final goodbye, but I wavered, seeking solutions to an unsolvable problem. Cheryl and Jenny both started shaking their heads in unison to get me to understand this. Jenny left and Cheryl grabbed my hand and then wrote "It's OK, darling, it's my time and I'm ready". That is when I sent word out and the children started their journeys to our home in Narooma.

I embarked on the carer role believing I was totally the wrong person for the job. On reflection and taking on board comments from friends and Cheryl, I now consider it to be the most important and rewarding thing I have ever done.

BUSTER THE CARER

Cheryl and I had dogs throughout our time together. They all became an important part of the family dynamic. We did not subscribe to the idea that, if there was a heaven, dogs were excluded as they had no souls. My sister Margaret, who has had dogs her whole life, was clear in her mind that there were animals she had known who were much more deserving of a place in heaven than some of the people she had met.

Which brings me to Buster and the role he played in Cheryl‚s illness, particularly the last twelve months. Cheryl has already given Buster some time in a previous chapter and this was because he gave so much comfort and support to her in her final months. Dogs love to have a role and Buster decided it was his job to be there for Cheryl whenever she needed him.

The more frail she got the less inclined he was to leave her side. When I would tell him to come for a walk he would always glance back at Cheryl to get her approval to leave before he headed off. As soon as we arrived back from the walk he would bound up the stairs to resume his place near her in the bedroom.

He knew she loved to watch his tricks and he performed them with flair and enthusiasm in order to bring her joy. As I broadened the range of tricks I taught him to get my socks from the ensuite wardrobe. Cheryl was impressed. I then taught him to go back and get my hat. When I extended the trick to get my undies, Cheryl wrote "That's enough it's becoming undignified".

As selfless as any person can be, it is hard to imagine a more dedicated effort of support than that shown by Buster our dog.

As she neared death Buster seemed to know as well as anyone that she was leaving. I have a clear memory of him in that time of taking a last sniff towards her before leaving the room the morning she died. This may seem a little fanciful to people who don't have dogs but I watched Buster mourn Cheryl in the weeks after her death, as much as any human. He would regularly check her side of the bed and look at me forlornly. He eventually decided it was now me who needed his attention. It was some weeks before he was ready to resume a normal routine after so many months focused on Cheryl's care.

Dogs are natural carers and are unconditional in the provision of their affection. For anyone facing a terminal illness you cannot put a value on that.

Clive Broman

A DECENT FAREWELL

Cheryl wrote notes for this book up to the very end; however, it is incumbent upon me to relate to the reader the nature of her passing. This only became possible after I had some weeks to reflect and had recovered a little from the shock of losing her.

Dr Jenny Wray, her GP, told Cheryl's story when she accepted the award for Telstra NSW Business Woman of the Year 2013.(You can find her speech on You Tube). Jenny referred to dying with dignity and it is important for people to understand how Cheryl was able to achieve this.

Planned departure, euthanasia, dying with dignity, call it what you want, it exists in various forms in our community. Cheryl and I watched the ABC show Q&A in the middle of last year and this topic came up. It must have been planned because the Rev. Fred Nile was on the panel and a more strident critic of euthanasia you could not find.

A young man rang in to put his case that he wanted to have some control over his life (and death) because he had an incurable and untreatable disease that happened to be Motor Neurone Disease. He was aware that the disease could take him to dreadful places where he did not want to go. Rev. Nile was very sympathetic and explained in detail how no one should have to suffer in our modern medical system. It was a matter of ensuring that people like this young man had access to the best possible palliative care.

Amanda Vanstone was also on the panel and pounced on Rev. Nile with an observation that she believed he had missed the point entirely. It was not about being in pain or managing discomfort with drugs. It was about being able to call an end when there was no quality of life – in other words, dying with dignity. It is a fact that with MND you can end up not being able to speak, eat or move any part of your body – and yet your brain will be totally aware. Some sufferers even lose the ability to open their eyes and of course have no way to interact. With the right technology these people can be kept alive for months or years but to whose benefit.

This young man had done his research and had made a reasonable conclusion, that he saw no value in staying alive under those circumstances. My wife Cheryl had made the same conclusion early into her diagnosis and was influenced by her experience of watching her father die from MND. The next question was how she could control the situation and she was relieved to discover that it was possible by setting up a living will and determining what interventions she would allow. She was quite specific about this and it allowed her doctor to provide appropriate and humane care whilst not prolonging her life beyond her wishes.

Neither I or Cheryl were unequivocal supporters of

euthanasia because it is a very complex issue and difficult to have a public policy that covers all the circumstances that occur. It is certainly a very difficult issue both ethically and legally for medical professionals to deal with. But deal with it they do, every day in hospitals and homes all round this country. Unfortunately because of the legal environment they take risks that someone could accuse them of acting illegally.

Cheryl wrote a living will in which she outlined very clearly her wishes regarding medical interventions. By doing this she provided her doctors with a road map about what she wanted to happen as her condition deteriorated.

Towards the end Cheryl could not take nutrition through the PEG without creating a dreadful choking reaction. She did not want to be put on a ventilator and she did not want to be resuscitated. For her life to be prolonged she would have to have been admitted to a hospice with significant life-support technology. It was her choice not to do that. I admired her for it because she never wavered from her decision once she had decided what she wanted. She was also aware of the impact a terrible death would have on those left behind. She wanted to be remembered for the person she was.

Cheryl and I both read books about people with MND who in the end were basically unable to move any part of their body and required massive medical intervention and a high level of care for their every need. The decision to continue life under these circumstances is understandable and very much one for each individual. There are all sorts of reasons why people want to continue to live when essentially there is no quality of life, but Cheryl was appalled at the prospect and hence her very clear instructions. I agreed with her but it still takes courage to make that decision.

The subject of death and the process of dying has been written about by many more qualified than me but the actual experience of it was not as I imagined. Until I went through it I didn't really understand the concept of death being a part of life and how it could possibly be a positive thing.

Cheryl had asked me to be with her when she died and I was a little fearful of how I would manage it. The fact is we were both unsure and afraid of that great unknown. But it was privilege to be there knowing she was accepting her time had come and seeing the peace with which she approached it. As I sat listening and feeling the changing rhythms of her body over the three to four days it took for her to die, I knew she was relaxed and thankful because of my presence and that of her family and friends.

I had written the little poem "First Impressions" on the train travelling to see Cheryl at Macquarie Hospital during her last stay a few weeks before she died. It was not a great poem but she did like it, perhaps because it took her back to the time when we first fell in love twenty-seven years earlier. In any case a couple of days before she died she could no longer write but gestured urgently to her friend Marg Falls that she wanted something from the top drawer of her bedside table. Marg found the poem in the drawer and Cheryl clutched it to her chest and made it clear that no one was to remove it. She was taking this one item with her to the "great beyond". She could not have given me a greater parting gift.

She was in a comatose state much of the time but still managed to squeeze my hand or give a smile and reassure those around her that she was OK. We all thought she was very close to the end when she suddenly sat up and asked for people to come in for a final goodbye and a hug. She was choosing to leave her body on her terms and it was a powerful thing to witness.

Ryan, my daughter-in-law, is Native American and she did a smoking ceremony moments after she died. I don't pretend to understand all that's going on there but I can say with certainty that people felt a wonderful energy in that room. I still feel good about the room now and that is a blessing.

I know people do not always die this well but it is important for people to know that it can be a positive experience. I held her hand and watched her draw her last breath. I experienced awe and great joy when I watched my children born. Watching my partner die was a similar experience with the joy replaced by sadness. I guess that reflects the reality of who we are and how we come and go on this earth.

For those who like the idea of serendipity there were two things that occurred on the day she died that are beyond my explanation. The van that came to our house to collect her body had the number plate CF-088 - her initials and the lucky Chinese number. If during her lifetime she had chosen to have a personalized number plate, CF-088 would have been perfect.

Doug Woodhouse made a note of the time she died, 11.17 am, for the death certificate. Later that evening he looked at his watch and realised it was frozen on 11.17.

OK, it just needed a new battery but timing is everything.

EPILOGUE

I understand that many people after losing their partner have some sort of mystical or spiritual experience of farewell. I had a dream about Cheryl and we were partners again.

We were in a Bond-like movie running across a barren landscape trying to escape from these rocket-shaped balloons that were pursuing us. In a movie cliché moment we said we had better split up to try and evade our pursuers. Then I stepped back out of the movie and observed Cheryl being trapped in this village street and having to fight her attackers. She was doing OK with amazing martial arts skills but eventually the numbers were too great and I watched helplessly as they started to beat her up.

Suddenly a car pulled up and the good guys came to the rescue (I am guessing the Israelis) and grabbed her and bundled her into the car and took off.

I was taken aside and told she was OK and had reached the safehouse. I left the house and walked down a yard to a small bungalow at the back. I walked in and Cheryl was just in the process of getting out of the bath. There is something quite beautiful about a woman getting out of a bath. Anyway, as she reached for a towel she turned to me and in a gesture put her hands out to display her bruises from the fight. She said, "Don't worry, I am OK they're just bruises" but then she smiled and pointed to the place where the PEG had been for twelve months and said "Look, it's gone". I went over to her and started to pat her dry with the towel.

I woke up and had a wonderful sense that she was OK. I know the mind plays these tricks but it was nicest thing to happen to me since she died.

It is now some three months since Cheryl died and, as you would expect, I struggle as I try to establish a new life without her. Only someone who has lost a partner would understand the daily adjustments that have to take place as you imagine a world without the person you loved and shared your life with. The initial devastation was mind-numbing and I now look back and wonder how I managed to do the most basic things, like getting out of bed.

However she would not be happy with that as she was very clear about the need for me to get on with life and not be too maudlin. She was right, as each day gets a tiny bit better.

Just when you think you have put a full stop on her story another thing happens.

An Aboriginal woman we used to work with dropped in a few days ago to pay her respects and fell to pieces as soon as I started talking to her. Bev is a pretty tough cooky, but she was taken by surprise by her grief and she said, "Jeez, I haven't cried like that for ten years". She had run into another Aboriginal guy in the local bakery who told her about Cheryl dying. The guy, Brett, was a client from four years ago when we did the South Coast Employment project. At that time we had just placed him in a job and he rang drunk at 7.30 one Sunday morning saying his life was over: he had had a complete meltdown, had wrecked his car and thought he had ruined the job we put him into by getting drunk at the Christmas party.

It would have been easy and reasonable to say we would call in and see him on Monday when he was sober and try and sort things out. But Cheryl knew this was a critical time for him so we jumped out of bed and drove down to Bodalla.

He would not talk to me but Cheryl took the beer off him and asked him if he wanted to see his little daughter grow up or did he want to go back to a life of alcohol and unemployment. She gave him a big hug and said she had faith in him and we rang his boss the next day who agreed to take him back. We arranged with Paul Nixon to lend him a car for three weeks while we got his car sorted out. He has now been there five years and is buying his house. I believe Cheryl, in a sense, saved his life. I suspect he does to. He was a decent man, Brett, who really just needed a chance and have someone believe in him. I had forgotten all about it but he hadn't. However the story tells a lot about the way Cheryl lived her life and also how she approached her death.

The book has been an important part of the grieving process for me. It did need a lot of work editing as Cheryl wrote much of it in the last few months of her life and concentrated on getting down her thoughts without worrying too much about organising into chapters and such. The fact that she had the energy and motivation to do this close to the end of her life is astounding. I have worked as best I could to try and produce the end product she would be happy with. I know that finishing the book is part of the process of accepting her loss. Cheryl's book was written in the last twelve months of her life. As she has said, the original intention was as a letter to her two boys,

Ashley and Paul, to give them a record of their mother's life, given she was going to be departing before her time.

She was also very aware and concerned about the fact that she may have passed the hereditary MND gene on to her boys and she felt a need to provide them with a legacy that was positive. Her interest and passion for MND research was based on a belief that with the progress being made, her sons would face a better outcome than her if they happened to inherit the MND gene.

Cheryl worked with great determination to get the book done but as often happens when writing, particularly as an amateur, it is a learning process and she realised there was perhaps a wider audience than her family. With the encouragement of others she started to expand on the issues, such as living with MND, and became a bit more reflective about the journey she had made since diagnosis.

Cheryl and I knew the prognosis for MND was on average about two to three years but even so, the final months came up quite quickly until we were suddenly aware she was running out of time. I gave her a commitment to write up and include some of the topics she had not completed. I found notes on her iPad and in her notebook that she had not had time to include in the manuscript. Thus the book, which was Cheryl's, was finished after her death and she was aware we would attempt to self-publish for friends and family.

As part of the editing process in the months after she died I realised there was a postscript and I felt motivated to add my own thoughts to the final book. I had already written a chapter that she had asked me to contribute but I then added a couple of chapters on how she died and the legacy she left behind. I admit this was a part of the grieving process for me but it also emerged from the many comments people made about how inspired they were by Cheryl and the way she approached the end of her life. It is impossible to process this until after you have actually lost your partner but I think that in order to understand her life, the reader needs to see the way she approached her death.

I was encouraged by a number of people to include a chapter on my role as a carer, not because I was very good at the job, but because it might help other people who get thrown into that role with no preparation and no choice.

Finally I put together a number of appendices, which emerged soon after she died that contribute to an understanding of the women she was, whilst helping to show how a terminal illness can still result in a positive journey for the person diagnosed as well as those left behind

I have been done my best to try and honor her wishes and finish the book.

There is a consistency to what people have written and said about her. The terms dignity and grace appear often in comments, as does her concern and interest for others. She would be mortified to be eulogised in death beyond what she was in life but she did focus outside of herself to the very end. She wrote to Dr Dominic Rowe three days before she died apologising because she could not donate her body to MND research because it was impossible to do so from Narooma.

She wrote individual notes to friends and family as well as sending countless emails and SMS messages to people in her last week. She was very worried about our friend Gerri who was about to have a mastectomy and sent her notes to build her morale a few days before she died. The note she left me contained some final thoughts and advice that was inspiring and unexpected.

I have been monitoring her phone and email and inevitably have been contacted by people who were unaware that she had died. Dealing with those people by phone and email is difficult but important. There is also the odd person in the street who stops me to talk about her; I find that very tough, but would not have it any different as I know the courage it takes for people to do that.

The donation she made with her son Ashley to the Macquarie University Research Foundation was matched by Ashley's employer Macquarie Bank, and after her funeral, a memorial was established at the MND Research centre. Her memorial has now raised over $25,000 and is a source of some pride for me. People are still contacting me to make a donation. We can only hope that it contributes toward an outcome that sees the end of Motor Neurone Disease.

Cheryl and I had a great love for watching movies together. I recently watched a magnificent music documentary called *Searching for Sugarman* about the singer, Rodriguez, that I recommend to everyone. It was an emotional story and I realised for the first time I could not share the experience of a wonderful movie with my friend. He sings a song called, "I think of you", in which he sings "My days now end as they begun with thoughts of you". I suspect this will always be the case for me.

It's a gentle sadness supported by the knowledge that a dreadful disease such as MND could bring out the best of Cheryl and the many people close to her. If her story helps one person, involved with a terminal illness, to manage a little better then that is all she could hope for.

Clive Broman (December 2013)

NOTE TO READER

The appendices contain a lot of material from the body of the book. For example Cheryl and I worked on her funeral farewell speech by extracting material from the book that she wanted to convey to those attending her service. The decision was taken not to edit these speeches to remove repetition because they have an integrity and meaning of their own. Her friends and family were keen for this material to be included as is.

APPENDICES

࿐

EULOGY
DELIVERED BY LYDIA MORTON 11/09/13

Dear friends of Cheryl and Clive

Doug and I live in the house just there and Clive has asked me to say a few words today about Cheryl and her life.

Cheryl faced her long illness with courage and dignity. She never gave up on life. She took the approach in her mind to be living with MND for the three years of its grip on her body.

Cheryl told me that her illness had made her realise that to be loved was her greatest privilege and pleasure. Her family and friends were the most important things in her life.

She said that, in the beginning, she would wake up in the morning and think that the MND was just a bad dream. But then her failing body confronted her with the knowledge that sometime in the near future she would pass "into the beyond" as she called it. Living next door, we saw Cheryl every day as she went from a slight speech impediment through the cruel corrosion of other physical capabilities.

She always said that losing the power of speech was the worst blow. She was a great communicator with a dry sense of humour, a born story teller. And as the MND progressed, she said that she wanted to say to people the things that she thought and felt about them. She said she knew this may well embarrass them, but, after all, "what the hell" she wrote. And she was very perceptive. She wrote me a very loving note a few days ago, which revealed to me a lot about myself.

Doug and I have known Cheryl and Clive since 2006. When we met, they were burning off the undergrowth on their then empty block. It seemed to us that there was only our garden hose standing between our house and a bush fire. Cheryl assured us that the local fire brigade was in attendance – then we met the local fire brigade, their good friends Bruce and Bill. Doug decided his own role was to stay clear so as not to get burnt alive and to provide a constant flow of beer.

Since then we have come to know Cheryl and Clive as much more than friends and neighbours. As Cheryl described it: "There is a level of trust and affection between the four of us that is unique and you don't come by those sorts of friendships too often in life. To me, the two of you are kin for I know that being of the same blood does not ensure love, trust and respect." We totally agree.

We have had many days and nights of fun and laughter in Narooma, Canberra and on holidays. Cheryl and Clive visited us when we went to the Netherlands for three years. They enjoyed all aspects of our lives, from the formal to the hilarious.

We had wonderful holidays together. In Bora Bora, Cheryl's favourite overseas place, she taught me how to snorkel – although never quite how to put the flippers on in the water. That may not have been her lack of teaching skills though.

We sailed round the Whitsunday Islands in a beautiful yacht. By that stage Cheryl could no longer speak and was fed up with writing notes, which arrived too late to be relevant to the progressed conversation. But every so often, from the cabin where Cheryl was reading, a note would be passed up through the porthole with a comment, which would correct a fact or cast a new perspective on our conversation.

Our last sea visit was to Lady Elliott Island on the far south of the Barrier Reef. This was Cheryl's last snorkel, and, knowing that, she had great pleasure eyeballing Nigel, the island's tame fish, and holding the shell of a giant turtle as he swam off into the blue sea beyond the reef.

Cheryl had a varied and successful career. From high school in Wonthaggi, she went to Darwin to study nursing. She had been the chief housekeeper for her family since her brother was born. She was then nine years old. Her mother was an exacting taskmaster. Cheryl scrubbed the lino on her hands and knees and prepared the evening meal. With these cleaning skills and her caring nature, she was a natural nurse. She told us very funny stories about the idiosyncrasies of her patients and her friends at the sisters' quarters, in a funny but sympathetic way.

Her son Paul came along when she was twenty-one, during her final year of study. Cheryl and Paul spent a hard few years living in a caravan, with Cheryl a working single mother.

Cheryl eventually joined the Northern Territory Public Service where she advanced quickly up the ladder. It was there that she met her future husband David Fong, son of a long- established Chinese family in Darwin. Paul became a member of the Fong family too and Cheryl's extended Chinese family remained very important to her all her life. Cyclone Tracy blew away Cheryl and David's house and all of their possessions. Cheryl, David, Paul and, soon after, Ashley again lived in a caravan. After the breakdown of her marriage, Cheryl and her boys moved to Canberra and Cheryl continued her rise through the public service, once again dealing with all the difficulties faced by single mothers, especially in the 1980s and 90s.

Her devotion to Paul and Ashley was the centre of her world and dictated most aspects of her life. As their sole parent, she felt entirely responsible for them. Cheryl had dreamed of travelling overseas since she was a teenager. She decided to set off for a short visit to Israel and the Greek Islands. She left Paul and Ashley at home in Darwin with friends. While the boys were quite happy in Darwin, Cheryl felt that her trip had been an unjustifiable self-indulgence. She said more than once that, "I was their mother and I should have been there for them, no matter what my own needs were."

David's family, especially his mother, Granny Fong, continued to include Cheryl and her boys in the family. Wanting the boys to be near their Fong family, Cheryl eventually moved back to Darwin. She was still in the public service and made some very good friends there. Several remain great friends. The most important is Clive, who became her best friend and then her partner for the rest of her life.

Cheryl has admitted that on meeting Clive for the

first time, she asked her colleague "Who was that garden gnome?". Clive on the other hand had a much more romantic view of Cheryl. With Clive's permission, I read you this poem about his **First Impressions.**

She moved with a steady determined grace.
Like many women of beauty
She seemed unaware or her impact.

The shoulders straight, she seemed taller than she was,
More tough times than easy had given her a strength and a fragility.

She spoke with private-school eloquence, but no airs.

Was it a severity or just that "singlemother" seriousness that comes with the need to get it done day after day, every day?

If she looked you in the eye and put her hands on her hips, LOOK OUT!
Next she was flaring the nostrils and it's time to flee, but could she maintain it if you made her laugh?

And when she did laugh, a lifetime of responsibility would melt away to reveal the delightful woman beneath.

I knew she was interesting,
I knew I liked her and enjoyed our moments,

What I didn't realise was that I had fallen in love with her.

The relationship was not easy in its first years. They had to deal with social and professional censure. Building a blended family with five children was not easy. But with love and determination they built relationships of genuine affection. Now both Cheryl and Clive are immensely proud of their two daughters (including Emma) and four sons, and the interesting, decent people they have become.

Cheryl maintained her love of travelling. Once all the children had grown up, she and Clive enjoyed visiting places known for good diving, as Clive had introduced Cheryl to the joys of snorkelling. They met people who became firm friends.

Their most notable overseas adventure was a two-year posting with the government to Guangzhou in southern China. Clive had encouraged Cheryl to apply for the posting, but Cheryl had been most reluctant, regarding herself as unqualified and "not good enough". Clive quickly found a job in Guangzhou and they enjoyed the travel within China, the friends they made and their insights into Chinese culture. As regards Cheryl's doubts about her capacity to do the work, my friend, who was the Consul-General in Guangzhou at the time, tells me that Cheryl was the most competent immigration officer on her staff. She had excellent people skills with both the Chinese and the other office staff, she was well organised and she had the highest ethical standards.

On their return to Australia, Cheryl and Clive spent some time in Canberra. Then they both decided to retire from the Public Service and move to Narooma, "where life is as it should be". They bought Cooinda Apartments and worked hard to build up the business. They sold the business two years later and were able to start building their dream home. They continued to swim and take their boat on spear fishing trips. They were a formidable hunting team for unsuspecting fish and could often be seen emerging from the water at Glasshouse Rocks with enough fish to invite us and other friends for a fish dinner, cooked in one of Cheryl's fabulous recipes.

I want to farewell Cheryl with some words spoken to her on her last birthday in June. I think they represent how all of us feel about this unique woman.

We think of all the wonderful aspects of your personality and in particular the Cheryl who brings so much joy to those of us who have been lucky enough to be able to consider you a close friend and mate.

We see your unconquerable spirit, a spirit that lets you meet your challenges with great courage, honesty, dogged persistence and genuine dignity. It is a spirit that has seen you through the most difficult of times as you travelled, and continue to travel, the highway of life and, it is a spirit that we who know you, acknowledge with unabashed respect.

We admire your sensitivity as you see needs in others that are often not seen by us and we appreciate the way you quietly respond to those needs with your soft touch and gentle understanding. It is an understanding that comes from the heart, based on wisdom, life experiences, wise judgement and an inner strength that you Cheryl have in great abundance.

We respect and treasure your uniqueness and we feel honoured to know such an extraordinary and truly beautiful person. We all agree, that there is no one else like you.

Cheryl, we want you to know that we cherish you for who and what you are and that we love you.

CHERYL'S FAREWELL

卐

(Prepared by Cheryl in the last week of her life with Clive's assistance using material from the book and adding some final comments so it could be delivered at her memorial service)

DELIVERED BY RUTH PERRET

Cheryl wrote a short message of farewell and Clive asked her if he could include some of the forward to her book on living with MND as part of her message.

MND is a peculiar disease in that it doesn't follow a set pattern in any one case. It can start in your upper body (bulbous onset) and take away your speech and your ability to swallow or it can commence with a gradual loss of function in a limb. No one can tell you how long you will live or even how the disease will progress. Some people die in a few months – Stephen Hawking the British phycisist has been afflicted for forty years. But on average you have two to three years.

There is no cure, virtually no treatment, except for a drug called Rilutek, which on average extends life by about three months, although it's hard to measure accurately the effect the drug has on any individual. Three months is not a long time but you can do a lot in that time with the right mindset.

The other drug which anecdotally seems to help is

cannabis but because of it is illegal in Australia there have never been any serious clinical trials. Not being a drug user at all I had to use my step-children to tap into the market and it was quite a laugh to grow, cultivate and use cannabis along the way.

I believe Doctors voted MND as the disease they would least like to contract. I am not sure why but I suspect it's because it chips away at your capacity as the Motor neurons start failing in their job of stimulating muscle movement. Essentially this means a steady deterioration into paralysis while your mental capacity remains intact.

I have talked about MND but it is a topic that others have written about with much greater expertise than me. My journey with it is very similar to that of others, not so much in physical symptoms because they vary a lot, but certainly in my emotional responses to loss of function.

In my case I can no longer speak or eat because my tongue is paralysed and my swallow reflex is practically gone. I now feed through a tube directly into my stomach. I also have a serious problem with excess saliva, such that I need to wear a surgical mask with tissues to catch the constant and copious drool.

Amazingly I can still walk around although I tire easily and my hands are getting weaker. If I was to see this to the bitter end, barring an early bout of fatal pneumonia, I would be a prisoner in a paralyzed body. Luckily for me I don't have young children like some other MND sufferers have, so I don't have that sort of motivation to stick it out.

The natural response of someone diagnosed with a terminal illness is to fight the disease. You so often hear terms like, "his battle with cancer", and "she fought it to the end" With some illnesses a positive mindset and a preparedness to endure radical treatment may win the day. MND is not like this, and I concluded early in the journey that I needed to live with the disease rather than "fight" some battle I was destined to lose.

The reality is that MND always runs its course and you don't survive but it doesn't mean that you have to give up on life. In fact in some ways the MND diagnosis provides opportunities to enhance the life you have in ways you could not have dreamed. The relationship with Ashley and Paul has gone to a level that I didn't imagine possible and provides me with comfort to my soul.

I am not pretending it is not very confronting to know you are going to die. Most of us know that to be the case but we cope because there is the uncertainty of when and how it will happen. It is not on people's minds on a daily basis. This is my point about living with MND rather than battling against it. You use your energy to live the life you can rather than trying to maintain the life you had.

My favourite activities of recent years have been my perennial love of reading and movies, snorkeling with Clive and spearfishing with him, my summer vegetable garden and making things with the produce. I still love to cook for Clive and friends even though I can't eat or actually try what I am cooking so it is amazing when I am making up a dish from my head that it actually turns out.

I think that I may have had my last snorkel, I won't have the energy or dexterity to do the vegetable garden again and even with the cooking I can't do it every day now. But I am reading a lot and watching movies and of course I have taken up writing in a limited way.

After awhile you don't yearn for the functions that you have lost you just adapt. What is harder for others to understand is that socialsing just becomes too taxing and you start to withdraw into a smaller world. Even though I have an electronic speech program and can write on a pad, in a social setting you are always too far behind the conversation, then you no longer see the point of commenting. I am not complaining, just explaining how it goes.

In my case I have lived a very full life since being diagnosed. Despite the rapid onset of bulbous MND to my upper body I have maintained capability in my limbs throughout. This meant I was able to travel and walk and swim without any impediment other than some fatigue. It also meant I have been able to look after my personal needs independently. MND patients can be in a wheel-chair within three months of diagnosis and yet still be able to eat, drink and speak. I am not sure which situation I would prefer but I am not complaining about the way things have played out for me. Each type of MND presents its own challenges.

Quite recently things have started to get a bit tougher. It is no longer easy for me to get enough nutrition through the PEG tube. The excess saliva issue which has plagued me from very early in the process has now started to impact on me more critically. A day hardly passes when I don't get a choking cough that wracks my body and makes breathing difficult. I can reduce the coughing caused by mucous build-up low in my throat, by not feeding but my body needs a litre of the formula food a day to survive.

My neurologist and friend Professor Dominic Rowe

once told me that there are two things that get you in the end with MND: nutrition and respiration issues. I am fighting both at the moment. I know in my heart of hearts that unless I solve the feeding problem my time is limited. I have been busy putting my personal affairs in order including the final editing of this book.

Someone asked me recently if I am fearful of dying, and yes, I am but I hope that I will be brave enough to call an end when there is no quality of life left. I am getting close, as I am not too keen on socialising or leaving my home now. I am sorry to my Narooma friends for my recent withdrawal. I am very tired after more than a year of communicating every feeling, need and conversation in writing.

It is quite telling for me that I have almost (but not quite) given up caring about the maintenance of our home. I started writing this story as a long letter to my sons Paul and Ashley Fong. However a number of people said I should write about myself and my experience with MND. So I used what I had written for them as the basis for this story, adding and deleting as appropriate.

To my husband Clive thank you for loving me for nearly twenty-seven years, helping to raise my boys and being my best friend. You always had faith in me and took me to places that I would never have dreamed of. I have travelled without you before but I always knew I was coming home.

This one is a one-way ticket into the unknown, probably oblivion, but who knows. Don't fall to pieces or be sad for too long. There is another woman out there who needs your love as much as I did and will love you back. You are not a loner and that's OK. There is life in the old Bear yet and joy to be had, so go for it with my blessing. Just take that squeaky bed we have put up with for 11 years to the tip first.

"I don't know how I have been so lucky to have such wonderful family and friends.

You have all helped me in many ways to make my life with MND more bearable.

I am not extraordinary or particularly brave; in the end you just make the best of it.

Laughter and tears help a lot. The laughter buoys my spirits and the tears clear the air.

This quote appealed to me when I read it.

> *"And did you get what you wanted*
> *from this life, even so?*
>
> *I did*
>
> *And what did you want?*
>
> *To call myself beloved,*
> *to feel myself beloved on the earth.*

> – Raymond Carter

And dear friends I have been beloved by Clive, our 6 children and all of you.

I die a happy person".

CHEZZA

Cheryl also received many emails and SMS messages in her last days. I have attached a couple of these that struck a chord and helped her face the unknown so courageously.

MESSAGE FROM TOM CALMA

Dear Cheryl,

For days I have tried to write to you but each time I have tried, I have been overcome with emotions thinking about the good times we have shared in Darwin, Canberra, Vietnam and Narooma.

You nursed my grandfather, loved my family and treated us not only as friend but also as family. Sharing time with you and Clive has been special, albeit for short durations most of the time, but it has been quality time and it has always been fun.

My memories are so vivid that they bring a smile recounting so many good times. I remember old Darwin hospital forty-five years ago and the young nurses walking the paths between the wards and the fans blowing to keep patients cool - life was not complicated in those days.

I remember the Chung Wah chicken sartee brigade and those wonderful smells and the beat of the drums and gongs. I remember the vain efforts you made to try and teach Heather and me how to make yu yem and we could never do it as tasty as you could, without a recipe and without any fuss.

I remember how peeved you were when I dissected the mud crab before cooking it but also the fun times we had working in the kitchen preparing for another banquet or me taking over to cook my yuccas or making yucca fish patties.

Sharing gardening stories and swapping the odd plant will stay with me and each year I will plant another crop of your vine tomatoes and I just remembered I still have to get some of your black Russian seeds for sowing this summer. Doug and I will have a cook-off each year to produce relishes like you shared with us but I bet they won't have the same kick as yours did.

But my greatest memories are how you and Clive spent so much time with Alice really getting her comfortable in the water down at Glasshouse or Bar Beach or Mystery Bay or even at the mooring. She has remembered her times at Narooma many times over the years and, like all of us, wish they weren't so brief.

As the moon rises we wish you a long and peaceful journey swimming with the whale sharks and seals and giant rays; just drifting in the serenity of an ebbing tide along the boardwalk as you did so many times with Alice while we walked on the deck and watched you float towards the horizon. We love you, Cheryl, and each month as we witness the birth of the new moon and watch it grow into the fullest and brightest moon we will be thinking of you, our true and loving friend.

Love Tom XXX

MESSAGE FROM LACHIE CALDER

I just spoke to Lisa and she said you are not doing so well...

The amount of faith you have shown in me over the short time I have known you has been incredible: To have such an accomplished woman believe in me has been the greatest support I could have ever asked for.

So I offer you my thoughts about a failing body containing a vital consciousness, a topic extremely close to my own heart and something into which I have put a lot of thought.

We are given the greatest gift at birth and that is our chance at a life. It's not a tragedy that the atoms created at the beginning of the universe need to go on to fulfil other roles... the air, the ocean, the trees, the ground. There is only ever a finite number of them. We and they are part of a huge cyclic process and the true tragedy is when someone is given life and it is taken away early or suddenly.

I know that you have been through some very difficult times in the last couple of years, but you were actually given an opportunity. This opportunity was to dot the 'i''s and cross the 't''s of your life, and from my perspective you have done this with the usual Cheryl care, tact, precision and attention to detail.

You have done the things you love with the people you love, healed wounds, made peace and sowed seeds and that is such an amazing gift to be given when your atoms are signaling that it's time for them to do something else. However, the suffering will be over soon and you will be back to your original, eternal state within the earth's boundaries. Your and my beloved universe will never let us suffer forever.

The loss of you will be devastating to all of us, particularly to your husband and your sons. But that is not something for you to concern yourself with. Life goes on and grief is just a human's way of celebrating the life of someone important to them. We need to be allowed that emotional display, but we also must carry on and figure out the future. Clive has his family and friends to look after. Paul and Ashley have careers and dreams to fulfil. Lisa and I have children to raise (hopefully?!!). It will all work out. Life is never easy and never, ever straight-forward but it always works out. The universe will not allow us to suffer forever.

I say this to you from the absolute core of my soul, Cheryl. I won't sing mantras in your honour or pray in churches for your soul's safe passage to heaven, because I don't believe in any of that. But I will remember dancing with you on the deck at your house in Narooma and I will remember how to to make jioza dumplings, but most of all I will remember your belief in my ability to do good on this earth while I'm alive, just like you did with your life.

Thanks for everything

Love,

Lachie

NAROOMA NEWS ARTICLE

Published 25/09/13

My wife Cheryl Fong died recently at her home in Narooma.

Cheryl and I came to Narooma 11 years ago to run the Cooinda Holiday Apartments. Like many people who come here to live we were attracted by the glorious natural beauty of the area. We fell in love with the place and spent countless hours snorkelling at the various beaches around town. But it turned out to be much more than just a pretty beach holiday town. It is easy to find fault with small towns because of the limited services but we both found there was a community we had not experienced in the city.

Cheryl was diagnosed with Motor Neurone Disease in 2011 and although we had some fun travels, Narooma was the place we returned to and where she lived with the illness. She was looked after in style by the girls at Mosaic and the Narooma pharmacy, and served with patience and humour by the people at Woolies, the NAB and other shops and services in town. She still loved going to her favourite restaurant, Sorrisos, after she was unable to eat. She even made the Narooma news with a prize bream we had speared.

Throughout her illness and especially at the end she received excellent care and support from health professionals Dr Jenny Wray, community nurse Steph Ratcliffe and psychologist Lisa Freeman. Our friends and neighbours rallied around to help throughout her illness and she never felt isolated or alone despite knowing she had a terminal illness. Cheryl wanted me to publish this endorsement of Narooma as not only a great place to live but also a decent place to die.

Clive Broman

Cheryl June 2013

If you wish to donate to Cheryl's website for research into Motor Neurone Disease, go to the website below and click on MND Research and follow the link to testimonials.

http://awc.alumni.mq.edu.au/